A MURDEROUS AFFAIR?

A MURDEROUS AFFAIR?

Stacey Whatling

Troubador Publishing Ltd
Unit E2 Airfield Business Park,
Harrison Road, Market Harborough,
Leicestershire LE16 7UL
Tel: 0116 279 2299
Email: books@troubador.co.uk
Web: www.troubador.co.uk

ISBN 978-1-80514-407-6

British Library Cataloguing in Publication Data.
A catalogue record for this book is available from the British Library.

Printed and bound by CPI Group (UK) Ltd, Croydon, CR0 4YY
Typeset in 11pt Minion Pro by Troubador Publishing Ltd, Leicester, UK

Dedicated to my mother, Betty Jerman 1922-2010,
to whom I owe so very much and by now,
I can sadly no longer thank in person.

1

An Amuse-Bouche

The planes on the face of a lover change with the relationship. And never more so, from first sight, the split second of falling in love, to the last… even to murder. That first look, that catch of the eye, the lithe flicker of a curving lash, the discreet upturn of the lips, the return of the glance, to the last, to the withdrawing of the soul, the chilling flesh as life recedes, the rite of death begins.

Of course, at first glance, first sight, it was never intended that murder would be committed. It was the last, last thing to be considered, if indeed thought of at all. Ridiculous too to think at the outset that I might become trapped like an insect in amber resin, the very glue of someone's affection, for all time! No, more than that, I was almost, in a reverse of all that is natural, I was almost umbilically tied to the man!

But that was not how it was meant to be. No, no, when I first saw him, all those years ago, back in the very early eighties, there was such a jaunt in his step, such a welcoming smile, and something else, something more, something special for me. In those split seconds of meeting, our eyes meeting, that slight widening, that shock of recognition, attraction, the pulse just starting to race, the thought of time just cast away… like you do so carelessly when young, seconds of life just tossed over to ridiculous things, in the passage of a lifetime, almost unnoticed, but for me on the outset of a mad, mad, maddening whirl of existence… there was something else, a secret something, something tantalising. Something extra. Something that stuck fast… like treacle, like glue, drawing you in, like quicksand, just as an insect in that age-old resin.

Gerald was one of those men who adored women, just adored them. And they in turn flocked to him, responded to that adoration. He was apparently so interested in them, in their problems, in their personal lives, what they were doing, that they collected about him at any gathering he went to, bees around a honey pot. Like the elephant, he did not forget those intimate conversations, at least with those with whom he truly connected, truly cared. I have seen many a woman, steeling herself beforehand against his reported charm, despite herself, flutter an eyelash before she was hardly aware she'd done it, succumbing in spite of her good intentions. Easy charm? Like Bill Clinton, who rose, as Gerald might have dryly observed (sarcasm well to the fore in Gerald's view of President Clinton's Oval Office antics, envy well hidden), to such prominence in the nineties, he had it by the bucketload, accompanied by a ruthless streak, too. He'd remember every last detail, in his words, he'd "work to the far end of a fart and where it comes from", and a secret… well, that was his trade: secrets, connections, the tiniest seemingly insignificant detail of someone's life that could be stored, could be later used, could be profited by. He was like a magpie, collecting things, people indeed, stealing things, ideas, phrases, storing them away in his nest for later, to be mulled over, savoured, produced again in the full blaze of publicity. Something secret, something extra – that's what I had seen, become so unwittingly attached to. Secrets: he could keep a secret and many people down the years brought him them by the lorry load. Secrets were the tools of his profession, storing them, cherishing them, judging when to bring them into the limelight. Professionally discreet always, as long as it suited. But personally discreet? No, he was not personally discreet very often.

Ever the frustrated thespian, I can hear him even now urging me: *Set the scene, Sweet, give me the scene, make the picture speak to me, for God's sake stop the flannel.* And he would take up a pose, half-joking, of someone languorous, exhausted, draping himself over the nearest bit of furniture, waiting to be told the news. Deceitfully, he would listen though; that is while his body acted that one part, his mind was honed to another, listening, hearing the secrets, hearing the message behind the words, between the lines, hearing the bits he was being told and those he was not. So let me set the scene.

Once upon a real time, that meeting, that first glance, was twenty-two years ago now, in 1982, just at the start of what became known as the greedy decade, the me, me, me period. Money and the making of it was the new religion. Mrs Thatcher was enthroned in Downing Street, sure of her position, coming surely to the height of her powers, just about to send the ships off to the Falklands. Funny isn't it, how women remember dates, those quiet anniversaries of the heart? The important things in life – where I was when

Mrs T left office or Diana died – no, but a romantic date, a birthday, an anniversary? Yes, always, as if your life depends upon it. It was a day in April, in London, very blowy, very fresh, the wind coming off the river. I remember there was a feeling that London was becoming once again the place to do business, as fashionable as it had been in the Sixties, though for different reasons.

The meeting finished, people gathered their papers; I gathered mine. I was standing over a wholly inadequate bag, forcing a ridiculous amount of paper into it, when a voice said: "Here, let me help you with that." Rather surprised by such a gesture, I looked up, showing that surprise, and there he was, those eyes, the mole rising on the crinkle of his smile, all open-handed, all fresh to the room, all full of himself and his news he was about to impart. What was it? I can't remember now. Funny, how lovers normally remember every last detail, nuance about their first meeting. I remember the month and the year but otherwise I was so taken aback by him, by that second glance returning and returning again to look at me, by the shock that somehow I had added to the pleasure of his look, I can't remember what the news was. Did he shout it, discreetly impart it? No, of course not, there was little that could be described as physically discreet about him. Or often, discreet about us. Even later, well, in truth not that much later, when we became lovers, sometimes it seemed he could hardly ever see the need for restraint in public, for discretion in public places. Is this a male trait – do they see themselves as invisible to the world, if they so desire? "So, they whisper of us, do they?" He'd throw his head back, all the planes of his face impetuous with daring pleasure, with his great leonine mane of hair, and such a lofty air, 'they' being so far below him. "Well, dammit, let them shout," and he would wrap me in a huge bear embrace and I would have to pinch him, in some increasingly well-endowed but above the waistline place, to get him off me. In private, that was different. Love is different in private. And so is death.

What a fool to be taken in by it I was! And how innocent! How did I not see, from the start, that I was the alternative course, not the pudding, but the savoury, to complete the meal? Think of Little Red Riding Hood: *And what big eyes you have Grandma...* See just how I was taken in, utterly beguiled. But no, oh no, no Mills & Boon story here! It outrages me to think of it now. But then, but then... how I was taken in, how I was charmed, jinxed, beguiled, call it what you will. Be honest then: fooled! And to think along the way, the places we went to, the things he took me to, the very span of emotions! Twenty-two when we met. I was so green. But at forty-four, when it was over, what a different person I had become. It is plain, of course, from the well-trodden, embittered vantage point of Age – with its partner in crime, Experience, producing that well-known offspring, 20/20 Vision – that it would all end in tears. But at the beginning, dear God, I thought we could walk the very heavens! Indeed, I swear Gerald thought he did.

Gerald worked in the City. 'Worked', that is, in the loosest sense of the word, as you may recognise it now. The City back then was on a completely different planet in a completely different universe compared with now. He 'worked' with a lot of others: well tailored, well paid, the product of overeating, good cigars, fine wines and people who 'do'. Gerald did not 'do', in the basest sense, only on an exalted plane. Gerald connected, he publicised, he promoted, he brought people together; in the jargon, he facilitated. People don't do that in quite the same way now – they pay a company to do it for them – but in those days, the early eighties – probably coming to the end of such an era – Gerald knew other Geralds who knew other Geralds, and if you wanted something done or bought or managed or sold, you contacted Gerald. Personally. It was in the time just before the scandals that hit Lloyds were about to be headline news; before the machinations on the Stock Exchange that caused the problems of the late eighties or beyond. Things were changing then, but in Gerald's circle, things were more charmed, calmer, a port in a storm, scandals there to be ridden out, the publicity usually a welcome and, sometimes – well in truth, usually – a manufactured by-product.

Gerald was a mover and fixer, though you would never ascribe such a lowly description to him to his face. A man with apparently catholic tastes, he would arrange a lunch, an outing somewhere in the Season, Ascot, Henley, Goodwood, a night at the opera, the Garden in the West End or Glyndebourne, though Gerald never stayed after the first act (off somewhere candlelit in close association with female skin). He was known as a Good Chap to Know. He liked to think of himself as a patron of the arts or rather, in Gerald-ese, A Patron. Presumably when with the closely associated female skin during the second act, they discussed Impressionism. He impressed her? What nonsense! I have been too long with Gerald's euphemisms. He impressed himself into her more like! They had sex. But that is my bitterness seeping in. Like a wine stain on a white tablecloth: easy to produce, difficult to remove.

Of Gerald, you would never see him in a game of golf though, never anything like football or even rugby.

"Something of the masses about them, Sweeting, something for the masses," he'd airily dismiss them. The diary pages of the papers loved Gerald. He was ahead of fashion, spotting the growing interest via magazines such as *Hello!* and *OK!* in soap stars, gameshow hosts, pop stars, footballers and their wives, as well as later, in the tailend of the nineties, reality TV contestants. As communities continued that move away from the front-doorstep cosiness, the twitching net curtains, the discussion over the garden fence, we all began to become faceless within our environment, symbolised ultimately in Mrs Thatcher's out-of-context but famous quote "There is no such thing as society," and referred dreamily back to through John Major's rose-tinted glasses, of cricket on the village green, spinsters on bicycles and warm beer. As Gerald would recount, as though lecturing, famous people became the neighbours, television soap stars 'her down the road', and gossip on an international scale – in terms of its setting at least – overtook and overwhelmed that of the corner shop, the pub at the end of the street. "Gossip," he would say, "like cockroaches, will survive a nuclear holocaust." And Gerald was there – it is true, never massively or very famously successful, but predicting it would happen – riding the crest of the wave of interest, intrigue, ingenuity, in getting gossip stories about such people into the right places. "A celebrity with a secret," he would state repeatedly as if I had never heard it, "is walking a knife edge. My part is to see that knife edge buttered. Preferably in my bank account!" For Gerald, these people's lives had become more saleable than the antics of the Royal Family, particularly after the death of Diana, Princess of Wales, when briefly the press reined its excesses in. And Gerald was very skilled at keeping the press hungry, massaging the story. When you are promoting someone (in Gerald-ese, that is making the world fully aware of your star/ product's potential or a share price), you have many such titbits to be fed piece by careful piece, to the waiting hordes to keep your rising star's name or product in the public eye. At the end of the day, as the deadline to go to print approached, journalists would call Gerald, anxious for a lead, a hint or a whisper, anything they could turn into a paragraph or make a story of, to fill the page. Answering their prayers, Gerald would always be a certainty for a story for that night or morning's paper. As the fly fisherman plays his line to get his salmon, so Gerald could feed a line, a murmur, a suggestion. Enough to build a paragraph on, leading perhaps later to the netting of the catch, to the full-blown exposé. The *London Evening Standard* then would produce several different versions of the paper over different times of the day. Often, I remember him buying the lunchtime paper, the *City Prices*, then the *West End Final*, all of them virtually similar versions of the same paper, and again and again turning to the gossip column, 'Londoner's Diary' or the City page, seeking his lead, his titbit of a hint that someone else had made into a story. Countless times in later life, I have thrown away such papers, yanked open, turned only to one page, the rest completely redundant, the pages still stiff and complete, virginally untouched other than that one page where Gerald sought gratification, confirmation that the story was headline news. He was anxious to see that his stories, his hints, were in print, too impatient to wait to see the press cuttings that Wendy for Wendon-Davis Associates kept as an archive. Many, many times I remember over breakfast, and from behind the morning paper, he would congratulate himself at sight of a headline or a picture. "I do give good copy," he would murmur happily (Gerald-ese as a private joke for oral sex). "See, Sweeting," he would sigh, warming to one of his favourite themes, "people are not so interested in crime anymore, or stories about ordinary people like them. The readers want a bit of glamour, a bit of sparkle, something out of the common run. They want to be taken out of themselves, see how the other half lives. Celebrity," he would intone as though speaking before thousands he hoped to convert, "is the new aristocracy."

For Gerald, making cash out of other people's lives was not an ethical consideration; précising him, we are all prostitutes in the pursuit of money – it is just that the ladies of the night deal in flesh and comfort, transact in words and touch, rather than a manufactured product and bills of lading. It all comes down to the two Cs in the end: connection and cash. Gerald was there to facilitate the connection. The cash would follow. "As a man follows a pretty woman, Sweeting, so night follows day," he would murmur, as if I had cause to doubt. Sometimes, Gerald himself was the story, though not always in a manner he might desire: "Not a good shot of me, not my best side, eh, Sweet?" he might murmur, looking at a photo of himself leaving a nightclub or a restaurant in the paper, before looking up and catching sight of himself in a handily placed mirror and smoothing away an imagined fault in his hair. The press and he danced along together – parasites, I suppose, in the same game, feeding off each other insatiably, the good stories and the bad. Supping with the Devil means more than just taking chocolates along for the host.

No one could tell me then, at the start of it all, in those first careless seconds, how I would come to live through him, that life would become him, to be hurt so often by him and then to miss him so much after, well, what happened, happened. Now I cannot bring to paper the pleasure of the touch and warmth of skin on skin, that utter liquid, honeyed joy of being held against him, of the world being kept at bay for an hour or so, deep in the comfort and delight found in his arms, a safe haven against the stormy wind and waves outside the harbour of his encirclement. Is it possible that happened or did I dream it? Of waking in the night, the wind wild outside, but under the duvet, to sense all that scented warmth and to snuggle up (yes snuggle, a lovely old-fashioned word signifying much comfort), safe against his sleeping body and, soothed, sleep on. There are not words sufficiently eloquent to do such a pleasure justice. A woman may take many to her bed, but there is one lover who stays with her always. Whatever he does, however he treats her. What foolish beings we are. There he is, in her mind and in her heart, if not with his body. And he was mine.

I shall miss his letters, of course. I shall miss that huge loop on the tops of his 'H's and his 'J's, as though one had all the time in the world to go round each letter of the alphabet, just as he had fashioned it so lovingly, so lingeringly, on the paper. All those letters, masses of them down the years, all tied in ribbon now. I shall miss his words every May, for the cow parsley, though of course, he never called it that: "*This weekend the lanes of North Norfolk are edged with Queen Anne's lace.*"

Anyone else would have settled for cow parsley. Or not noticed or commented at all. But not he, no, no, nothing so commonplace, nothing less than flamboyant overacting.

Queen Anne surely had nothing to do with cow parsley but to Gerald there was no other description.

Or later in the summer, written something like this:

It being August, the swallows are already gathering on the telephone wires in the field behind the house, like the quavers and crotchets on a sheet of music. Presumably there is a process of identification going on, to somehow facilitate the journey back to southern climes. The butter pats in the field behind us are now being collected. The farmers certainly work very hard at this time of year. The next thing will be the muck spreading and then ploughing. Thankfully the fields are not burned anymore. That would be a worry as well as very unpleasant if we are downwind of it, as is usually the case.

'We'. 'Us'. Hmm. Don't like that, didn't like that. We. Mr and Mrs Wendon-Davis. Not a simple name, no, nothing like Smith, or Johnson, or Brown. Mr and Mrs Wendon-Davis. He and she. He would leave me and sometimes go home to her. Mrs Wendon-Davis, the MP. What had she done to deserve him? Had she known his vows would consist of "To love, honour and betray," would she have married him? Who knows? It was not my place to ask; that was part of the inner sanctum of their relationship, not mine with him. And to ours, he never brought that old and ridiculous adage, 'my wife doesn't understand me'. Which, of course, she did, perfectly. Indeed, to be fair, he rarely mentioned her. No, it was only in letters, love letters you might otherwise call them, that he forgot himself and included her. 'We', 'Us', 'Ours', all inclusive words and I was not included – as far as she knew, but he knew all right. He set me up in a flat with her money, paid for the flat too – not rented, not borrowed – all of it and he put it into my name. How daftly kind is that? He sets me up for life, with her money, and then, and then… what happens, happens. Let us not get too ahead of ourselves. Let us not muse here on whether that happening was accidental or meant to be.

And since I have mentioned it, let me tell you about the flat. Just a word, for now. It is at the top of a tall and elderly building near the Haymarket in the West End that suffers in the lower extremities from damp and cat pee, and in the upper, from the attentions of the local pigeon population. Gerald was oblivious to all of that. "Location, Sweet, my darling," he boomed at me. 'Location', as if this was some magic elixir that compensated for much. Certainly location was directly responsible for the rubbish that accumulated on a nightly basis despite the best efforts of Lady Porter's Westminster Council in the late eighties, the rats from the vast and growing collection of restaurants and fast-food outlets in the vicinity, and, once, a tramp who settled in the gloomy and secluded alcove by the street door to the flat for a month one autumn, taking advantage of the sheltered spot. The light over the door never worked for very long and, remarkably, no one ever thought of calling an electrician to check the wires. After Friday nights there was always a selection of used condoms lying about the ground, which I took to picking up with sugar tongs, kept just inside the front door on a hook for just such purposes. And once, coming home on a Saturday night, I found a rather drunken couple in what looked to my by-then-practised eye, the advanced stages of copulating al fresco against my front street door. Imagine politely asking "Can I just put my key in?" at the crucial moment. The door was never quite the same again, after what was quite a vigorous battering. Gerald, of course, saw none of this damage, dismissed it even. "Hard at it, were they?" he asked, an eyebrow raised in amused affectation and disdain. In reality, he was fascinated and now I remember him enquiring with as much casual insouciance as he could muster: "Set the scene, Sweet. Was, she, the girl, I mean, was she pretty?" I clouted him for that – what possible relevance was that? Chuckling, he moved deftly out of range. Otherwise 'Location' prevailed as the lodestone, overwhelming all evils. For Gerald, time, circumstance and location were all the blood of life, the definition of his existence.

And however much he was in the gossip pages, the very picture of slightly ruffled elegance, in the diaries, society updates, somehow along the way, in tandem with Mrs Wendon-Davis's oh-so-helpful cash, presumably, he appeared to make money through his contacts. To Gerald any publicity was good publicity. Gerald at forty, for example, was heralded in a headline *W-D at 40*, over a picture of him, it is true to say, looking rather sheepish and holding a can of the world-famous oil. Nothing seemed to be too ridiculous, though it is true that he did smell rather oily, like a mechanic, for the rest of the day. That suit was never quite the same in his eyes afterwards, but the publicity was great. In a sense, he was like the God of Connection; the papers loved him because he could connect with people and he loved, craved, created publicity. But not for Mrs Wendon-Davis. There was a line. She was like a goddess on a pedestal. He did not look up to her, he just put her there. After all, she kept him.

I shall miss his surveying a restaurant, his hand under my elbow, propelling me forward, towards the *maître d'*. It would be impossible for the poor man not to find us a table; by the time Gerald Wendon-Davis had stopped propelling me, we'd be otherwise stranded in the middle of the room with the *maître d'* up against the opposite wall. Of course they found us a table. The best table. How was it always free? How naïve of me to even ask. And usually, a glass of something very cold and white, usually French but later New World, would somehow arrive, to my eye unbidden, but apparently chosen by some long-distance perusing of the wine list. When I grew wise to this, I could gauge the planning in it. We would always arrive to the sound of, or be propelled towards, a table accompanied by foreign sputterings of: "But *Monsieur*/*Herr*/Mr Wendon-Davis," – depending on the restaurant and the nationality of the *maître d'* – "er, er, how unexpected, how..." Or depending on the nationality: "'ow *very* nice. What an unexpected surprise." The expression of 'very' seemed always italicised, particularly when I realised the pretence. The numbers of 'er's and the degree of surprise helped me towards this realisation. But the pretence was maintained. Gerald would always answer with a drawl, under an air of exquisite distance, feigning ignorance at all costs: "Indeed, Carlos/Andrea/Herbert," – again, depending on the nationality – "how *very* nice," as if the emphasis on the word 'very' sealed the secret between them. If the restaurateur was there, it would be 'Mr Franks', or whatever the man's name was, but the pretence of a surprise visit would be maintained, accompanied with the accompanying wink Gerald would give, which the *maître d'* somehow always returned, thinking I would not see, and the very large tip Gerald was always at pains to be seen leaving. The *maître d'* would bow very low as we left, the angle of his bow, like the Japanese, in direct deference to the size of the tip. Gerald always left a tip.

Often in later life, as we sat down, Gerald would giggle in anticipation and, sharing his joke about the booking of the table with me, murmur in a theatrical sotto voce: "Sweeting, on my headstone, do you think I could have 'he was an outstanding luncher, par excellence'? Do you think the stone mason would carve that?" And he would turn, still chuckling, to take the menu from the waiter, waiting attentively beside him for such purpose.

"Sir, a little something to start with?" he would say, clearly knowing – to the initiated – Gerald's habits. At the same time, somehow or other, the waiter would be signalling to his colleague, the sommelier, better versed in such things arriving in bottles.

"Ah yes, indeed, a bottle of something red and, I think… em… expensive to follow this, my man," Gerald would pronounce. "Perhaps something French today, do you think?" The sommelier would join us, his toes dancing in anticipation of a large bill and a thorough exploration of the wine cellar. They would discuss, at length and laterally expansively with great deliberation, vintages, slopes, vinters, wines known, bottles turned, the habits of the French, the New World, mergers, acquisitions. It was always immediately clear, even before that first glass of white wine arriving, that always seemed to be just right ("Forward planning, my Sweet, always forward plan, very important," Gerald might warn) that the sommelier and Gerald were old protagonists in a battle of knowledge about wine knowers, growers and drinkers. To the untrained eye, fooled till the realisation that

Gerald was always known (and expected) in the restaurants he frequented, food could almost be viewed a secondary consideration, though ultimately it would become clear that this was not so. A similar amount of time could be spent deliberating with enormous care and pleasure over the menu, and whether today's mussels were sourced from this particular tide bed or that, which hens had laid the eggs, the foie gras (goose or duck?), the birthplace of a cow, or the location of the particular asparagus bed and whether the stems were green or white. I began to notice over time that the waiters really did know their stuff, indeed presumably boned up on it before being interrogated. But, once the waiter had gone, the dishes determined, the accompanying wine discussed and viewed, the list of food whisked off to the kitchen, Gerald might chuckle, sipping his misted glass, his mind clearly still thinking along the same lines about his gravestone, as if the interruption of ordering had never occurred. "Or," he would wink at me, "a *bon viveur*! Yes, Sweet, I like that better, a true *bon viveur*, what do you think; do you think I could have that?" It was all rhetorical of course, but he loved the description, cultivated it.

Later of course, much later, when I realised quite what a complete fake he was, before the whiff of duplicity became a stench, when other women arrived on the scene, when my crow's feet began to lengthen, my upper lip began to pleat, and everything else began the departure south (and not just for the winter either), I would hear the arrangements made beforehand – the restaurant called, the discussion with the *maître d'*, the order given, so that the entrance would later be superbly executed, the same "er, er, Monsieur/Herr/Mr Wendon-Davis, how unexpected/*very* nice..." the number of 'er's giving away the lateness of the booking. There would be the same propelling motion committed, the best table always, "Oh, just here, sir," the victim – sorry, the new woman – amazed afresh at Gerald's influence, connections, contacts, so that even a table at a top London restaurant may become instantly available just at the sight of him. Or seemingly, at her with him. That chilled glass of something white would materialise and mist over as glasses of wine often did with Gerald, arriving almost unbidden. I remember as I raised it to my lips – looking at Gerald, he would often wink at me conspiratorially, when he knew I knew how it was all so artfully pre-arranged. By the time he had begun to move on from the initial conquering of me, he had mastered still further the art, so that the waiters would flutter round her, his latest victim, make her the centre of their dining perfection. It was only afterwards, alone, that she foolishly might discover, if she tried it, that the procuring of such a table did not work without him, underscoring his apparent greater importance and her stupidity at being taken in. Of course, she wouldn't talk of it to him.

Am I too bitter? Can I look back on all those wasted years? All that time waiting? Was I truly that person, a butterfly paralysed by chloroform, speared by a pin through the heart, waiting for my collector's return? He impaled me often enough. I soon speared him when the time arose. And I shall not be collecting him. Collectors are not normally collected. Did he set up every woman, like he set me up? My little flat, overlooking the river, convenient for quick and slow trysts, in between managing this meeting, making that one, a little lunch. "How's this for an aid to the digestion, my dear," as he'd come through the door (with his own key, of course). "Only got thirty minutes, come on, my lovely, come on." Remarkable, in a man of his size and age, how quickly he could undress (was there any Italian in him, for the quick getaway?), how quickly he could reach a crescendo (never an orgasm, that was for the lowly people), carry me with him ("Come along, my lovely, let's be adoring you"), dress and be at his meeting. As he went, he would kiss my forehead in a bemused way and mutter, "Satisfaction with every erection, eh, Sweet?" winking at me as he was leaving, fancying himself pompous and ridiculous by turn. Gerald was like a magpie, collecting sayings and witticisms. The one about satisfaction he had seen on the back of a van connected with television aerials. He had chuckled over it for days after seeing it. And typical Gerald, as he left me, in that turning to go, he would include a swift appraising and, probably, admiring glance in the mirror at his reflection before he left. Elegant Gerald – top marks. Always.

No, not a selfish lover, Gerald, not an ungenerous man, no, never ungenerous. Too generous, probably, far too generous too with his wife, Mrs Gerald Wendon-Davis's money. And his own gifts. Clearly far too abundant to keep for her or for me.

There was the time he was cited by a would-be starlet as the father of her child. This was a ridiculous accusation as the child bore no racial or any other resemblance to Gerald at all. Splashed across the front of the *Daily Mirror*, in the mid-nineties she alleged that he persuaded her "to play up and play the game", though the game was remarkably undefined. She went on (ringing Gerald on the quiet) to grab her own headlines very successfully and use them to jump-start her acting 'career'. She went along with all the stories, about the

Tottenham shirt, the rubber outfit and the toe-sucking, which I found hard to believe in itself as Gerald is so disinterested in football (the toe-sucking being another story), but it got her posing in football magazines, sometimes in Tottenham shirts, sometimes not even that. She became a seven-day Page 3 wonder. Shares in Tottenham even rose briefly that week as a result of the 'revelations'. The citation did her career no harm at all and Gerald enjoyed bobbling along on the current of publicity. The starlet was very grateful to Gerald. They exchanged Christmas cards and air kisses for several years after that, to say nothing of probably sharing beds and bodily fluids. It is distasteful for me to record such things but, having known Gerald so long, not wholly unexpected. At the time, nothing was proved, no one publicly got hurt, though I had much to say about it till he pacified me with an earnest, "Sweeting, it is just a bit of fun, a splash, a bit of an alternative way of doing business. There is nothing in it. Please forget about it." I wonder now what he told Mrs W-D. And in turn, what she told the party whips, who do not appreciate such publicity splashes about the husband of one of their MPs. What kind of damage limitation was employed there (one of Gerald's favourite phrases)? Who ranted at whom in those relationships? I wonder now if she was instructed to rein him in, tell him to be less alternative, less generous with his talents.

And therein was his downfall. There are only so many times you can rant at a man who has picked you out of the crowd, nay, plucked you from working obscurity, placed you in a flat at your (and his) disposal, made you feel like the only woman he ever looks at… and then you find the bills for places you never dined in (and neither did Mrs W-D), letters you never wrote (and neither did she) and, once, a photo of a girl in underwear you have never bought or owned. And it certainly wasn't Mrs W-D. Accused but admitting nothing, Gerald might mutter, with a wink, "A woman will draw you further than gunpowder will blow you," before turning away, the politician's answer – ceding nothing but giving a meaningless soundbite. But such questioning was pointless. Ranting is good for the crow's feet, good for the harridan. Fish wives do it. Politicians do it. Mistresses in decline do it. Sound and fury, signifying... pain, jealousy, betrayal. The loneliness of the mistress passed over for the duties to the wife is one thing, but for the mistress, passed over for the delicacies of the younger woman, what depthless, unspeakable hell is that? What is there to say? How long have you been seeing her? Are you sleeping together? How ridiculous – is the sun rising in the west? Have you taken her to our table at the Savoy, La Tante Claire's; are they laughing at me behind my back, your propelling arm? Worse of all, have you paid for her? But what is there truly to ask? None of it matters. Would you get the answer you wanted, that you could believe? When the time comes, there is another woman, and then another and another. Remarkably, we are all taken in, fooled, made to feel the centre of his universe. "Did I not mention Mrs W-D?" he says all surprised, as if you would scour (as indeed I had – and doubtless all the other women did too) the gossip pages. "Did I not say I was married, Sweeting?" as if you had not known his status, when you have arranged a weekend there, a night away somewhere, ridiculously taking it somehow for granted, hoping against hope he would be there. "Can't stay away, darling, got to go home, see the other woman," as though the other woman were some kind of joke, some kind of interloper into the afternoon twilight of the bedroom, that you have brought in, like something unsavoury, not his lawfully wedded, very rich, very duped wife. And glowing from his exertions, eye ever on the clock, far more skilled in the art of manoeuvre and counter-manoeuvre than I shall ever be, he would turn us both over and bring the run of his hands to bear, those twinkling eyes, the smile, to remove such ridiculous suggestions from my mind. There are no lies in touching, only bare facts.

Was it ridiculous that I knew all this, knew of the other women, indeed the utterly rampant womanising, yet I stayed? I suppose acknowledgement of such comprehensive womanising is rather like banging your head against a brick wall. In the end, you become numb to it. The first time I realised what he was doing hurt unspeakably. The first? What am I saying? The first, the second, the third time… Upon each discovery, in my view upon each betrayal, there was much shouting; this was before I knew shouting was worthless. I shed many tears and refused to see him, but he charmed me back. Thereafter, I came to realise that, for the most part, Gerald's dalliance among other women was rather like him having a haircut or changing his socks – it was just part of his life. Just like sneezing, only the hankies kept changing. Until one day, one day, far into the future, where he overstepped himself, chose a location for his tryst with another woman that was too close to my home, indeed in my home. But that's for later…

In the glory days, for indeed such there were, before the effects of time had moved down his face, made all the chins, slumped onwards down his body, before the extreme talents of his tailor were employed to such great and remarkable effect, yes, the planes of his face were, like the attributes of his character, loving, gracious, kind, generous. Ah, for the glory days, those wonderful, heady, glorious days, before time, too much good living, too many women, too much abuse… yes, he was very beautiful and generous with his talents. And the money. I must not stop here and say any fool can be generous with anyone else's money. No, I must record the great and the good, the fun, the loving. And I shall. But, spoiling my story, overriding it all, remember this thought, keep this with you as I take you through all the clichés of love. A wiser person than I said that those in love recognise the seeds of their own destruction. Along the way, having sown them, and so widely too, Gerald certainly tried his best to harvest them.

From that day in April 1982, it was to be a long relationship, long even in the milestones of a marriage by today's standards, some might say an inordinate length of time to love where there is no legal requirement or obligation. For just over twenty years, indeed from 1982 to 2002, we knew each other very intimately for what in any relationship is a huge span of history, a very considerable length of time. Let me put before you a series of tasters of how it was, or in Gerald's words: "Sweeting, a vignette, just a little vignette, just by way of example." For my part, think of it as a selection of tapas: fine at the time, but you wake up next morning, hungry, hungover, your mouth full of the aftertaste of garlic and stale wine.

2

The Start of the Affair

So where did we start? It was a day in April 1982, very blowy, very fresh, the wind coming off the river in London. Is an affair like a river? Starting high in the mountains, a rarefied atmosphere, miles from public places, the water seeps out of the ground, out of the ordinary run of things. It becomes a babbling brook (don't lovers babble at first?), the water rushing, helter-skelter, wiggle, wiggle, curving in on itself in the current, down the slopes, utterly engrossed in itself? What else is important in the world than the sheer joy of the flow, of being together, lovers combined, two becoming one? Midstream, the curves of the river widen, it becomes lazier, produces leisurely meanders, draws the river plain in, brings other features into the relationship. The river is no longer of itself, inward-looking. It travels on. And when the river gets to the sea, it has grown fat and weary and worldly wise, the spark has gone, the water is sluggish, and there is much rubbish in it. Channel clogging silt, so that the affair chokes – all that accumulated emotional baggage – and becomes suffocating before oozing out to the sea or is swept into the incoming tide. But all of this was miles from the start; this was the spring, the life birth of the affair. The estuary and all its murkiness were years away.

So. Set the scene. By now Gerald would be grumbling. *Come on, Sweet, get on with it.* My part of the meeting finished, people gathered their papers, I gathered mine. There was much chatter around me; Argentina had just invaded the Falklands. People were beginning to argue about fighting for the islands but there was some doubt between the men next to me as to their location; wasn't it somewhere off the coast of Scotland? Somewhere else in the room, I caught a snatch of talk of oil and the potential fields offshore from the islands. "Yes, sixty billion barrels thought to be there. We knew that back in 1974. It's in a basin to the north of the islands. Rather makes you question the motives for sending a taskforce, doesn't it?" The speaker laughed rather too loudly, in a very horsey sort of way. Thinking back now, he did have a very long nose.

Conscious that I had to rush back to the office to check my desk for messages, I was forcing a ridiculous amount of paper into a wholly inadequate bag, when a voice said "Here, let me help you with that," and rather surprised by such a gesture, I looked up, showing that surprise and there was Gerald, all open-handed, all fresh to the room, all full of himself and his news he was about to impart.

I smiled, hurriedly removing the surprise, changing the planes, and he – this then unknown and really quite beautiful man – brought his head down, his eyes concentrating on me, on mine. Such a glint, such a smile. He had a mole by his left eye and when he smiled, it rose. And his eyes were grey, dark grey. I was close enough to see his irises, great dark irises, expanding with pleasure as he smiled down on me. His breath warm against my cheek, he was so close, I could smell his aftershave, not a great wave of it, but like a scent on the breeze, after rain in the garden. Pleasant, warm, clean, soothing. Crushed lavender and something else, fresh-cut grass. His face was so close, I could almost feel the smoothness of his skin, I could see the tiniest details, a smile line by his mouth, a hair he'd missed in that morning's rituals. Still looking, unexpectantly intently, still seeing those irises smiling, a part of me – a very tiny part it is true – was just becoming aware of my embarrassment, at a smile beginning to be smiled too long for normal business use, when he leaned forward still further – could he get any closer – and lifted my bag, and me actually with it, to make it easier to get the papers in.

I shall never know now whether anyone else noticed: did the room really quieten for them too? Did anyone see then what he did next? Did it register? He leaned forward and said quietly (never discreetly): "Let me have your number, let's lunch. Let's do it. In fact," as though it were a new thought, "let's do it today."

As though it were a command. As if he were granting me a wish. And he leaned again to pick up my hand, not shake it, but squeeze it – such an intimate gesture in a public place. I could almost taste his breath, a faint scent of coffee, then the aftershave washed over me again, almost like his shadow. There was suddenly a dizzy feeling in my brain. I had never met the man before. Never even seen him, smelled him, certainly not touched him. But here he was, huge, beautiful, apparently utterly intent on lunching with me. "Wait for me," he urged, "I'll just finish here quickly." He stood back and put an elegant index finger to the side of his nose and dropped his eyelid. In the dizziness of the moment, it took me time to realise it was a wink. And I didn't even stop to protest, let alone argue. The Devil had got my tongue. In a thrice, the arrangements for my afternoon dissipated, the here and now became much more important. Lunch! That same day! No talk of the then-unknown Mrs W-D then, safe from the vagaries of her spouse then, tucked away as she was in the House, listening to Mrs Thatcher's jingoism. Not that I knew anything of the connection between this beautiful man and her then but, if I had, from the ladies' toilets, sorry, powder room, in a conveniently nearby restaurant, after the first propelling and the knowing *maître d'*, there was a radio, broadcasting rather quietly from the House of Commons. If I had stopped to listen, I might have heard Mrs W-D speaking in her crisp, authoritative way, one of the few women recognisable in Mrs Thatcher's overwhelming shadow. This was only 1982. It would not be until 1989 that Parliament was televised when I could see her, if I had been minded to stop and watch, sitting not two rows behind the Prime Minster, in that daft crowding they adopted in the Commons, to make the chamber look better occupied than it actually is, for the television viewing public. In her bright-green suits. To make a visual as well as an aural statement. Whilst all the while, her husband made different statements elsewhere. With other women. Many other women, as I discovered.

But before that, Gerald delivered his important news. My part of the meeting had finished. The room was reassembling for the next part of the meeting; people were reordering themselves, their papers, the sitting arrangements around the room. All was calm, orderly.

Despite the apparent and sudden change in my fortunes for the day, I got to the door, turned and took stock; I watched. Gerald was a flamboyant and large man. I have always thought he must have fused bones in his spine or, at the very least, across his shoulders as he had such a stiff and large upper torso, as though he was constantly shrugging his shoulders. He had such a distinctive body shape and large chubby fingers, it would be hard to imagine two of him or to miss him in a room. Later, I would think that if I had to describe him to someone who had never met him, I would say that he was the Bill Clinton of connections – that once he was in a room, he was impossible to ignore.

But for now, stepping forward towards the table in the middle of the room, into the limelight, as you might say on stage, he waited in a wholly theatrical manner for silence to descend on the room. As he stood – balancing, almost dancing – up on the balls of his feet quite evenly, I was able to admire the dark pinstripe suit, clearly tailored to the contours of his strong, solid back, rising over his buttocks, so that the double vent at the bottom of the jacket by chance revealed a brilliant underside, a yellow lining against the dark blue, rather like an exotic bird showing the down under his wings. As he moved from foot to foot, in the slight rise of his trousers, I could see yellow socks above dark, conventional City shoes, very highly polished shoes. I marvel now – years later, as fashions have changed, conventions have eased – at how rebellious even yellow socks were. But at that time, hard as it may be to believe now, it was clear that here was a man who secretly rebelled against the conventional clothes he was required to wear. So what else was rebellious about him, what else was different? There was something else, something secret. Or so I thought. Silly, innocent, naïve me. And see, see the insect and the resin, the insect beginning the dance, not quite stuck to the resin, not yet immortalised in amber. I was fascinated, even without the performance going on in front of me, presumably, I think now, for my benefit or to hide my departure.

On this occasion, he was very patient, waiting for the moment of quiet, before saying his lines. He had wide shoulders and a powerful back. The jacket fitted perfectly, moving against his shoulders like a second skin. In those days, his body was still taut and he was quite sleek for a large man. His hair was very controlled that day. It was a kind of mane, grey streaking into the very last of a glossy dark chestnut, all of it very thick, very bouncy, drawing the eye to it (*Wasted on a man*, as my mother might have sniffily observed). And it was well cut, not wild, not mad like Beethoven's hair, or unkempt as some men with such hair can be. It was tailored, like the suit, tailored to the man, who was still there, waiting and gradually the hubbub in the room began to dwindle, as the audience finishes its conversation as the house lights go down before the play begins.

He cleared his throat in a loud and theatrical way – this was all new to me then, in a relationship seconds old – and, raising his arms to gather the room in rather a messianic way, he delivered his message. "Ladies and gentlemen..." he began, rather as though making a formal speech. The sounds of the room finally died away. His smile dissipated the formality of his delivery and around the room there were smiles back at him, he was obviously known and obviously liked. He spoke for about two minutes. I watched as he began to carry the audience with him, how he made them laugh, how he was self-deprecating to win them over and of course, with his enthusiasm and charm, even in such a short space of time he did. The room was captivated. I remember it was good news.

When finally he fell silent, there was a slight hush before everyone realised he had finished and then the audience took its lead from him as he turned on his heel, raising his chin slightly, lifting his head as though to the spotlight again, right and left to begin to take the adulation in response, like a composer at the end of the first playing of a great piece of music, or the conductor at the Last Night of the Proms. Some of them before him even clapped. Small wonder that I cannot remember what it was he said. Into the general celebration of his news, a very low-key celebration certainly, I became aware of a new background noise. Gerald was still taking the adulation in a general way, smiling, nodding, saying something… even now I cannot say for sure that, as he stood there, he touched anything.

There was a terrible groaning noise, elemental, as old as the world, the groaning of wood on wood. The table – the centrepiece of the whole room, running almost the length of it, a huge, long, beautiful piece of oak on steel legs – lurched, buckled, groaned again. There was a sort of pause and suddenly, then slowly – but with such absolute inevitability, indeed utter finality – the whole table groaned again, as if in terrible pain before it slumped, collapsing down in a slow and dignified way at one end. The metal legs shot out under it, not dignified at all, accompanied by a loud clang, as in '*CLANG*'. I had read cartoon magazines as a child. The ringing sound – echoing, echoing, echoing – died away into the silence.

It was the end nearest Gerald. Had he moved? Had he kicked it? Did he step sideways? There was a hush in the room. There was more to come. We all watched, entranced, as the tabletop slowly reached the floor, like the tree it had once been, being felled in the forest. It looked for all the world like the dying pinnacle of a ship, going down with all hands. With an awful inevitable-ness, papers, cups and saucers, coffee, orange juice, several jugs of water, various calculators, a whole dish of biscuits, signified their cumbersome but unified response to gravity, and slid steadily and inexorably with great dignity down what had become a slide, to crash or plunge into a terrible pile of paper and fluids and crumbs, at Gerald's feet. Confidential documents, top-secret documents began to combine rapidly into mush, just like the oxygen from the sinking vessel rushing to the surface as the ship began to sink beneath the waves.

In the terrible quiet, Gerald, still pristine, utterly and inimitably elegant, raised his hands to his mouth in such a gesture of stylish horror. The stage was his. No one else had moved, cast in stone with shock. His movement was the catalyst for theirs. Now of course I know his reaction was fake, well, I am all but sure of his involvement, but how had he done it? The room, previously a murmuring hubbub, then the stillness as the calamity played out, was suddenly electrified. From the horrified silence that accompanies a disaster one can do nothing but watch, the room was transformed. After those few hypnotising seconds, where harmony, neatness, pattern, structure had been shattered before our very eyes, the room suddenly leapt into furious reaction. Everywhere was mayhem. Lawyers on hundreds of pounds an hour, chargeable to corporate clients all over the world, sat stunned, leapt to their feet, stood horrified. The charging clock was stopped, nay, it was sundered, shattered by whatever Gerald had done, unwittingly or otherwise. For it was, it must have been Gerald. All around us was chaos – suddenly where it had been quiet and orderly, people were shouting, some were laughing, people were rushing to retrieve papers and possessions before they intermingled and sank into the mire at what had been the end of the table but was now a soggy, sticky mess on the floor at the foot of the slide. Someone was on the phone, ringing for the maintenance men; someone else on another phone, ringing for the housekeeper to remove the mess and delay the lunch, which even now was on its way. The first trolley was framed in the doorway. All was mess, fluster, chaos. Where people had been sitting in an orderly manner around a table, now they were either still sitting, but apparently in the middle of a room around an upended table, a statue of a shipwreck, or on their feet, jumping about, making a lot of noise but to no great effect. And in the middle of it all, as attention turned to the culprit (had he done something, had he really kicked the table leg, had it been that loose?), so Gerald took the back-slapping, the "It had to be you," the jokes, the "Trust you, W-D," the mock rage, "You clumsy oaf," before turning away, turning back to meet me outside. For I had slipped away amid the mayhem, see how quickly I took on the role; leave the limelight to him, but wait for him just a short distance away, backstage, in a more secluded area.

Lunch, full of giggles – Gerald's "Did you see his face? And hers? Oh, I wish I'd had a camera; the room! Talk about the wreck of the Hesperus!" Gerald's denials – "It wasn't me, honestly" – with a twinkle in his eye, all the while his hand on my thigh. My thigh, mark you, my reputation meeting his hand, under the protection of the tablecloth. Do people normally do that on a first date? First date, eh? Some first date, it was only a matter of minutes after saying hello. A tad forward I fear, well very forward, I think now. Why didn't I impale it then, with my fork? Or one of those things you get the snail out of its shell with? Why didn't I stab it and raise it jubilantly aloft, like the policewoman did on the Underground once, with the hand of a man who had tried to take advantage? "To whom does this belong?" she questioned whilst the poor man (poor man?! What am I saying? Pervert more like!) could not save his blushes. Likewise, I could have raised it, and the evening paper that night that - long, long ago night - would have proclaimed: *Member's husband caught mid-grope at lunch.* The red tops the next day could have had a field day. *Member in House, husband stabbed with snail fork after attempted pull.* Or worse...

But I didn't. I didn't do any of those things. I was dazzled, insouciant with pleasure. And neither did any of the others after me. But stop now and ask yourself this: if Gerald had already done all the fancy arranging beforehand and thus been able to do the propelling bit - with the *maître d'* all an apparent confusion, before settling us to the perfect table - how had Gerald done it? Had he booked it and then gone to the meeting to select a victim, sorry a co-diner? Or is this my lately cultivated suspicion creeping in only now...?

Gerald was a major fan of Mrs Thatcher. In the course of that first lunch, with his hand still apparently lodged on my thigh, he looked deep into my eyes and told me: "We need a strong leader and," helping himself to the bread with the other hand, "if it comes in a skirt, swinging a handbag, then so be it." Remarkable how sex and politics combines so smoothly. Hardly surprisingly then that Gerald found her very attractive. "A very striking woman, she is, strong and striking," he stated as we ate the main course, staring at each other, making conversation in other ways than the merely verbal. Though at the time I did not ask how, he breezily said he had met her face to face and that, "In the flesh," – and he managed to make it sound as though she was – "she is much prettier than in the photographs." Later of course, it became evident he had met her through Mrs W-D, more than once presumably. Looking back, it was a funny way to start a relationship, discussing the physical merits of the prime minister, but then the invasion of the Falklands was on everyone's lips at the time and she was making the news.

Dessert was not the normal standard fare found on any menu in a London restaurant. Never mind the hand-on-thigh barrier, skilfully and speedily negotiated. Put into political bargaining terms, if you like, we got a long way towards a major treaty. Put crudely, we did not need spoons to share the dish we enjoyed. Put romantically, it is true to say that we exchanged more than numbers. Oh, put it how you like, I was young, I was 'the maiden bowled over' (Gerald-ese with a cricketing metaphor that was strictly speaking inaccurate that day, delivered in his case with a wink), I was blinded with the very impact of him.

Like the news he imparted after coming to my unrequested aid, I can't remember where we first 'came together', presumably some hotel room nearby, I should think. And though I can't remember now where the place was, there were two things about that afternoon that stand out in my mind. I do remember the cornice of the ceiling was truncated; the building was once part of one of those lovely old Victorian or Edwardian edifices, where the rooms are long and wide with big windows. Latterly, someone had seen fit to divide the room, in the easy equation of profit versus space, to increase the returns, so that the once lovely surround – a once golden cornice (the cream overpaint now peeling in one area), presumably once painstakingly chosen and made in a wholly different era – now disappeared into a blank wall, thrown up by some cowboy builder. The light, hanging down from the ceiling, was in the wrong place. No one had taken the trouble to relocate it into the new centre of the room. And the window, which once presumably had been sashed, was now something plastic, easy to maintain, but out of place. Surprising really, that such things had been allowed to happen on an old building, but it clearly had. Funny, how these things come back, when you would have thought I was being charmed and bewildered by Gerald. I did, after all, spend quite a lot of the afternoon on my back.

And the second thing, the second was the surprise when Gerald took off his shirt (and draped it over a chair – I remember that quite clearly), I found his back was covered in hair, which ran down to a sort of point, making the bottom of a triangle into the cleft of his buttocks. His chest on the other hand, was almost completely hairless. As the years passed, the hair on his back grew silver so that at times he looked like a badger. I remember once he had it shaved and it grew back all prickly. He only did it once, typical Gerald, "to try it out, it's the fashion", but the pain of it all growing again, the itch, was too much to bear.

But the story, back to the scene. *Set the scene, woman, can't you? Stop all this blathering about.* Gerald would be exasperated by now. Our 'coming together'. This is Gerald's coyness, schooling... some boarding school in his teenage years where sex was an unmentionable, in word, subject and presumably event. He certainly made up for it in later years. On my part then, after years of his euphemisms, I can do 'coy'. Gerald liked his women – me, at least – to be coy. Not to be too bold. But then at other times, rather like changing one's clothes to suit the occasion, he apparently liked 'rough'. But not for me, he did not like 'rough' with me. 'Sex' is for the lowly people, as per Gerald's euphemistic line of thought – see how he has rubbed off on me. I learned the euphemisms and even now, schooled over many years into them, it is a hard habit to break. And it is true we did come together, like an explosion reacting to a mix of chemicals. Someone even banged on the partition wall from next door. Shocking really that they banged, it was not that sort of a place. Thin walls? "Oh no," he'd say, "that would never do for the likes of you, my lovely. Tut, tut, no! We'll go somewhere better next time."

You can see how I was taken in. And that was the first time, I am sure, that I heard him say: "How's this for an aid to the digestion, my dear?" But that time he did not add the finishing part – that came much later, the "only got thirty minutes, come on". Who knows if he had a meeting that afternoon, or was it just a negotiating stance; he simply had become unavailable to whomsoever he was negotiating against. Note not with. So, this afternoon he did say: "Come along, my lovely, let's be admiring you." I wonder now if he said that to all the girls. But then of course, it was the first time I had heard it, and he did admire me. When you are young and supple and lithe and willing and the planes of your face are as yet unsullied with the army boots of time, of course you are there to be admired. Who, in their right mind, wouldn't?

With increasing age comes morality. What seems permissible at twenty-something – a very immature twenty-something I now think – by forty or later seems extraordinary, even shocking. Think of how intransigent old men become, as they realise that life is only a leasehold against, not the ownership of, immortality, and they grow anti the change of anything, muttering 'things aren't what they used to be', when as youths they were manning the barricades, militating against the immoveable, trying to overturn the world. So it was, here was a man I'd just met, lunched with, overturning me. I was now on my back, nude next to him similarly unattired, neither of us wearing much else than a smile, with him beside me, on top of me, inside me. "Our first pressing," Gerald called it later, as if I was olive oil. Now I marvel. Now, if that age, would I require an AIDs test of my potential partner before I divested myself of my clothes? Surely a condom at the very least? Back in the age of innocence, back in those early eighties, I didn't ask such questions; it seemed perfectly natural. As indeed it was.

At that time, Gerald must have been thirty-three though in the moment his age was irrelevant. I was not there to ask his age. He laid his clothes out carefully, no unforeseen creases, no unexplainable stains, nothing untoward. The jacket was hung over another chair, so that the yellow lining, the exotic plumage, was plain to see. The tie was folded over the shoulder of the jacket. The socks, those yellow socks, very unusual in those days when men dressed much more conventionally, were folded together on the seat of the chair. However passionate, however erotic, the next move had been executed by a perfectly tailored, perfectly unruffled man. Planning ahead, for the next appointment, whether with Mrs W-D or not. How did he manage to get his clothes off so carefully and then mine? Why can't I recall this? And then, our clothes prepared (mine too note) and laid out in a manner Nanny would have been proud of (yes really, for of course as I later learned, in the Wendon-Davis household of childhood, Nanny had held court, along with the requisite number of Labradors), he stood me back from him and yes, yes, he admired me, his head on one side, turning me gently round, rather like a man who is admiring a piece of china he has just bought at auction, having only seen it in the catalogue but now has it in his hand to turn it over and over, before impaling me, like the butterfly with the pin. Collector's item. That was me. To be kept in a rarefied atmosphere, the specimen drawer, admired from afar, kept with a harem of other butterflies - one can never have too many - and safe from the hands of other collectors. But I get ahead of myself again.

Back to that afternoon. The spring dusk came quite early, very gently, stealing over the room and with it came room service. See, the planning, the advance planning pays off every time. Later, Gerald might have said breezily, trying to impart some casual thought that I knew by then had been long in gestation, "One swallow can a summer make, if you use mirrors," or "Rome wasn't built in a day, because they didn't have plastic." Or some other daft comment, supposed to indicate his careful planning. But that day, I knew none of this. Of course I was impressed. We came to a natural interval; when I came back from the bathroom there was a bottle of champagne being opened, white napkin and all, by a nude Gerald. Had he opened the door to the waiter like that, I now wonder? But not then: I was young, this was a first outing. Wouldn't you be impressed? And strawberries, strawberries in March, totally out of season, a wholly mad expense. I expect at sight of them I made some inane comment, some youthful exuberance along the lines of "Strawberries! Wow! My favourite! However did you know?" as I ran to him clutching my fingers together in a kind of act of prayer, to open them out to embrace him in my joy. And Gerald would smile that artful smile, those lines forming crinkles around his eyes, the mole dancing in the upswell of his skin as it became an early crow's foot. He would have made some coy comment about knowing the needs of young ladies as his arm came to encircle me, draw me to him. Now, I would say they were tasteless, brought halfway round the world, nothing but skin and water, but then, that afternoon dipped in champagne, they were the fruit of the gods.

And he was a god. Age had not yet weighted him down, left its tracks over him early, bloated him, as it does to those in the City, leaving them richer but terribly aged while still young. Burned-out but opulent – or BOPO – was a phrase that came to describe some millionaire thirty-year-olds at the end of the eighties. But that spring afternoon, he was still firm and beautiful, a considerate lover, willing to play, willing to please, conquering gently, truly a god. Did the others after me think this? What of those before? Did they all get the champagne, the unseasonal fruit and for those who came to bed with him after me, by then it wasn't just the strawberries? Did they get the love-murmurings, the hands smooth as only a middle-aged, office-bound, never-sullied-by-manual-work lover's hands can be – lily-white, the nails beautifully manicured (once a week, in Jermyn Street; whatever the deal, the appointment never missed), the bespoke aftershave still gently wafting by? Were they admired, each in their turn, one after the other, after the other? There can be few pains more intense than wondering about those others. Why do it now still? Didn't I do it enough at the time, once I knew of them?

We went for what I now know as supper but was then to me a light meal. Should we have had that for lunch? Now, as per our American cousins, I might say what is the deal here? A man fills a woman full of food and then pounces on her; is that the civilised thing to do? Should she be grateful? Why do I ask all these questions now? That evening the restaurant was candlelit, gentle music filled the air; there were booths everywhere. I have said Gerald was never discreet but perhaps, caught in the afterglow of the afternoon (doubtless one of many and after which, he was, as ever, immaculately dressed) – still with the light of love in his eyes, his cheeks then tight over his bones – perhaps then he was discreet, the moth by-passing the flame of publicity for the subtlety of a curtained corner.

I remember we had eggs. Light, airy, like our moods. "I must see you again." He was all dramatic. I, well… what do you expect? I was taken in – that twinkle, that smile – I was transfixed by it all, like a child at the first sight of Father Christmas. No, that's not right, no, more like a rabbit in the headlights... And later, but not much later – he was off to an appointment (now I wonder was it the previous woman or another one he was trying out? I have become too cynical) – he kissed my hand away from the lamplight of the street and any waiting cameras (unusual for him), and put me into a taxi – my number safely tucked away within that immaculate tailoring.

3

Meeting Again

For a while after that there was nothing. I had begun to put the afternoon down to a dream, albeit a mad one. Then about a week or ten days later a letter came, the envelope thick, the paper that handmade rough feel, that makes the letter bulky. Big loops, lots of them, all over the page. Massive whorls over the 'h's, a veritable circuit of the page over the 'j's and the 'o's. I remember the envelope alone caused quite a stir at the office. It was of such a size and such a quality. And that handwriting, in such a black ink and with such a nib. Despite all the comments from the post room upwards, no one mentioned what kind of a person might produce such writing. There were no graphologists on the staff in that particular office, or rather none who were going public with such information. Perhaps, with hindsight, they might have saved me… and him.

At the top of the sheet inside there was the address of a house printed on the paper and the paper was cream, very thick, with a watermark. The paper even still smelt faintly of him. Crushed lavender and freshly cut grass. No one had said to me 'beware of a man who smells of crushed anything'. That particular one was not among my mother's selection of *bon mots* or old wives' tales.

He wrote my name, no term of endearment.

On Monday, I stopped at Blythburgh church – you will know this as the Cathedral of the Marshes. At night, even in winter, it is lit up from outside and seeing it takes your breath away. It seems so other-worldly. This day, it was boiling hot in that mad way that spring days can be, but inside as ever it was cool and the light was very good – the windows are clear glass and it somehow distils the quality of light, improving it and enhancing it. There was an art exhibition, but I was not really interested so much in that. It was the ceiling I wanted to see – the angels in the ceiling. The whole spine of the roof was decorated with them. Funny to think, amid that pure-white light off the walls that once all our churches were painted. It says in the guidebook that Cromwell's men could not reach the ceiling, hence the angels survived. At Ely, known as the Ship of the Fens, it was not so – after all, that was Cromwell's citadel, so presumably greater efforts were made to eradicate any images. Ely, while still very beautiful, is very damaged.

There was no reference in this first letter to what had happened that afternoon… what was it, a month, six weeks before? That is, our afternoon in bed, spent, as I was to learn in due course to call it, 'lovingly'. Why was it a guide to a church in Suffolk? Cathedral of the Marshes? I had never even heard of the place. I got a map out to check where it was, a small place to the west of somewhere called Southwold, on the east coast. Ship of the Fens? It was miles away, somewhere else, west, nearer to the Wash. What relevance was this to me? He did not write 'I am thinking of you'. But right at the end of the letter, he had written, seemingly very quickly as the writing changed slightly as if to impart the urgency: *Sweeting, I press myself to you.* Well he had. Several times one spring afternoon. An immaculate pressing.

Afterwards, he told me, as he had written, so he had been watched by Mrs W-D: she writing constituency letters; he writing love letters disguised as travel monologues. "Got to keep up the appearances, you know, my lovely. Wouldn't do to let the side down," was his explanation. The last line had gone in as he folded the letter. Not much time for loops and whorls, yet still he had managed it. There was a veritable Spaghetti Junction over the last 'o' in 'you'. I remember musing: *How did he manage that and keep the ink from smudging?* If I had been wise, I should have had the whole lot analysed, like they do in detective novels. Would I have recognised the alarm bell if it had rung? Do not ask for whom the bell tolls, if you don't want to know the answer. And I didn't, not then. Not till much later, with the stark, ice-sharp clarity of hindsight.

The house was in Norfolk, though it did not say where in the address – it was just the house name and the county. Later, I would learn where it was. *High Fold.* And underneath, *Norfolk.* As if you would automatically know where it was. I remember that, *à la* Noël Coward, I wondered: *Is there anywhere high in Norfolk?*

High Fold. Huge across the page. Like him, huge across the sheets, the Collector awaiting another netting. I did not call him that then – that came later. I wonder, to whom did he tell Mrs W-D he was writing? A fancy bit I have eased the digestion of, brought to admiration, used your money, or will do in the future, to install her in a flat so I can visit her at my whim? Oh, and keep her from other men, from the rest of her normal and natural life with another man? Was she so engrossed in her constituents she did not hear him?

But then none of this mattered. This was his last line, the one that really meant something, after all the rubbish about a church somewhere. *Sweeting, I press myself to you.* Like wine. I cherished it all. I was thrilled. He had remembered me, albeit I did not understand the rest of it, but I had been pressed and remembered. And later bottled. And if I had recognised it, still later labelled and put in his wine cellar. To fester.

Anyway, some more time had passed. Would another letter follow? It seemed an odd way to communicate, given the circumstances. You meet someone at the end of a meeting, spend lunch and a very intimate afternoon together… and he writes? It seemed an unusual way to behave, but then I hardly knew Gerald, I had only slept with him; sorry we had crescendo'ed together (this was only the start of learning Gerald-ese, then). But then, I met him again, or rather I saw him across a crowded room. What a cliché.

It was in May, shortly after publication of the *Sun*'s '*Gotcha*' headline about the sinking of the *Belgrano*. Everyone was talking about it, amused and shocked by the headline in the same breath. It was not really a laughing matter though; after all, 368 people had died in the incident.

In London, it was suddenly an unseasonably warm evening, even after a stormy afternoon. My hair was clammy against my skin. I worried briefly that such heat might affect the 'wings' of sprayed hair on either side of my head. I shudder now at the memory of that hairstyle. In the eighties, we were all so hirsute, men and women, but it was so controlled. In memory, you forget the appalling things of fashion, of how ridiculous we looked. In your imagination, you just recall how you felt, or the expression on someone's face, not exactly what they wore. It is rather like the statues in a cathedral, dressed in medieval garments because that's what their creators wore, the people who modelled for the sculptors. It becomes the norm. You just assume it has always been so. Photographs do not bear out this line of assumption. Photographs bear witness to the sins of youthful fad and fancy. Long after fad and fancy have been discarded.

Back to the story, Sweeting, Gerald would mutter. Still worrying over my hair, I remember fussing briefly in my bag for a mirror and giving up, exasperated. If the wings of hair dropped… well, so be it. The bottle of hairspray was back in the office. It would just have to do.

The tree blossom was blowing across the street as I got out of the taxi. I stepped into a huge swirl of petals, which were covering a puddle. One shoe became very damp. I am not an angel; I swore under my breath as I stumbled out of the flower-strewn gutter and onto the pavement. The lining of my suit was sticking to my back, it was so humid and it is possible, though I have tried to forget this bit, that my stocking may have just snagged against the metal corner of my briefcase. I paid for the taxi and tried in the lobby, unsuccessfully, to remedy a work-soiled appearance, turning away to a quiet corner to smear lipstick on after I left my coat with a large, round lady who appeared in a hole in the wooden panelling to take it.

The party was on the second floor. I struggled up the wide, carpeted steps, my wet shoe sloshing quietly against my foot, while clutching the cloakroom ticket I had just been given for my raincoat and briefcase. The room was facing west and was very hot; I was flustered and late. My face, never pale, would be red and probably shiny in the heat. I had only just managed to get there after a terrible day. My name was misspelled and the name-badge's pin stabbed my finger as I struggled to put it into my lapel.

With hindsight, how apt. Did I unknowingly fall asleep for a hundred years? With hindsight, we are all so wise. Fussing over the badge, mentally cursing the designer who put the pin in such an awkward place, I happened to look up and, like a heat-seeking missile, amid all those people, he caught my eye. Our eyes literally locked for a second… seconds; everything slowed. It was like being hit by a bullet.

He was with a crowd of men, his full mane of hair, as I have said, already distinguished grey to silver, winning the war against the once-glorious chestnut of his youth, even at thirty-three. People age early in London. My finger ached, diverting my attention. There was a balloon of blood. I was just delving into a bag to find a tissue when he came over. Did this man spend his whole life watching women trying to get into bags? How did he get away so quickly from those men? Was that a swoop or a dive he made across the room as he moved, as a bird of prey might, or am I just imagining that now?

Holding out a clean and perfectly folded, white, cotton, utterly pristine handkerchief to me, "Let me help you with that." He smiled, piercing me like an electric shock of pleasure. It was so nearly a repeat performance of early

April, only the time of day different. There was a smear of blood now on my cuff. As he leaned towards me, kissed me on the cheek, his eyes a-twinkle with delight, I could smell his aftershave, cool, gently redolent of a long afternoon spent touchingly. The warmth and the pleasure of it wafted over to me, very sharply, as though it were only yesterday.

"Hello," he said, in his best dark-chocolate, Rolls-Royce, purring tone, what I would later recognise as his best Richard Burton impression. It was a special 'hello' – all mine. "You have blossom in your hair," he said. "You look like the Queen of the May." Suddenly it did not matter. Neither did the blood. Or the wet shoe. Here he was, in all his glory: a dry-shod, elegant, unbloodied glory. He was still smiling with those perfect teeth... like a wolf does at his victim. No, no, I must stick to the facts, not run away with those I now see.

I smiled back; did the conductor in my head direct the orchestra then to prepare? What an incurable romantic I was. Well, afterwards, you know when you have fallen headlong into the chasm of temptation. It stretches across the path of life. Your mother always warned you against it. But you know best. What does she know of romance, of feckless love, of throwing caution to the wind? And at her age? She's always just *been*. Not loved, not foolhardy, not Young. So, regardless of countless warnings, you have to put your head over the edge, through the bars she has tried in vain to erect, protecting you from yourself, and you have to pitch headlong. And so I did. Years later (was it only a hundred years?), I climbed wearily back up the sides of the abyss, hand over hand, foot over foot, tired, cynical, wretched, well housed but so cheated upon. But as of that moment, all of that was ahead, unknown. What was so immediately apparent was here was this lovely man again on this May evening, so kind, so thoughtful, so caring and so apparently intent on absorbing me and being absorbed by me. And the young are so stupid, so self-involved. Why could I not see him for what he was? It is true only age brings true wisdom, but couldn't some older someone, in that room, have cut me off a slice of theirs and said: "Here, you look like you need this?"

So we sparkled at each other. The badge was forgotten, let alone the misspelling. He knew my name, indeed from memory he knew more of me than my name. At the thought, I could feel the heat rising in my cheeks. The mole by his left eye had risen to its zenith with his smile. I felt I was being pulled into the grey twinkling depths of his irises. Was there a chandelier in the room? Did we outshine it? Captivated by each other - well, in hindsight I was by him - he said: "Well… and isn't this a pleasant surprise. How very nice to see you again. You look more lovely than I remembered. Have you got a drink?" The rest of the room had fallen away. I heard the emphasis on the 'very nice' and the 'more lovely'. He had remembered me! His 'hello', his smile, was just for me. *Just look at that twinkle!* It was all I could do not to put my lips to his, to sink into oblivion, fold into the curve of his arms, forgetting the rest of the party. My mother would have said Leslie Phillips used the same tone to good effect in films of the fifties and sixties to young women of a certain persuasion. *Never trust a man with twinkly eyes*, she might have advised, along with thousand other *bon mots* I ignored completely. She wasn't there though; I was already falling into the abyss. Indeed, I was diving. With a smile.

We found a man with a tray of drinks, or rather somehow Gerald indicated to him and he came alongside us, Gerald still looking into my eyes. Gerald had a talent for such things, getting a drink to arrive while not diverting himself from you. Raising a glass to my lips, I was entranced by him, as a rabbit is by car headlights. Before being run over.

"Hello again and come to the balcony for some air..." he smiled, apparently knowing full well its effect on my knees, which had turned to jelly. Balcony? Was this a film? Was there really an orchestra? Could I hear violins? Do violins come with the champagne and out-of-season strawberries every time, or was it just for us? It had seemed such an ordinary room when I had first entered it. The evening had seemed so dull, so ordinary, a case of what came to be described in the nineties jargon as a networking opportunity: the exchanging of business cards; mundane conversation punctuated with polite but pretend laughter; the trying to hide the looking over the shoulder to see if there is anyone else more 'interesting' in the room. Not now though, not now. It contained Gerald, a veritable, sparkling jewel among men. The networking forgotten, normal life on hold, the evening was changed completely. I had pricked my finger, tumbled utterly into the abyss and a dream had begun. Once upon a time…

"What a pleasure to see you," he purred, as if I was something he, with the patience and eye of a high-flying vulture, had waited a lifetime to catch… sorry, to meet again. Putting his hand on my arm in what might be seen as a caring way but also in a commanding way – pulling me with him, towards him – he went on: "And how are you, my lovely Sweeting? How have you been? Did you get my letter?" I even thought he might stroke my hair, such was the concern in his voice, the look in his eyes. The desire to kiss him was almost overpowering. Was this the first time he called me by his nickname for me? Who knows? I had eyes for no other. Mixing children's tales (see how far into the abyss I had fallen in such a short space of time), I was Cinderella, he my Prince Charming. Despite all the odds, the terrible day, being late, the misspelled identity, stabbing my finger, I had gone to the ball. There would be a happy ending; after all in fairy stories, everyone lived happily ever after. Didn't they?

A girl came by with a tray of canapés. Gerald reached across and carefully selected one, rather as one might select a diamond. He lifted it to my lips as though worshipping there. Beyond his chubby collection of fingers, all I could see were his eyes, drinking mine. I opened my mouth, rather as a baby bird does at sight of its parent, entirely trusting, utterly confident what he was giving me was good for me. It wasn't. A quail's egg, then very fashionable. I hated them and worse still, this one was faintly curried. I swallowed it quickly, keeping the muscles on my face from the wince they wanted to assume. I was past caring, past rejection. If he had offered me poison, I would have consumed it, unnoticing. Next day, one of my colleagues, presumably from a standpoint across the room commented on my cow's eyes and Gerald feeding me. "That bloke," the girl sneered, "what were you thinking of, letting him feed you? Did you know where his hands had been? You know what men are like!" The office laughed. But that was later and just now I was too busy swallowing a quail's egg – a curried one to boot, a concoction that disgusts me even now when I recall it – and watching Gerald to care about anything else.

Thus he drew me, indeed waltzed me, it seemed, into the room (were there other people there?), and we talked and laughed, our fingers danced with each other and I was his prize. *Look at me*, his face said publicly, *look at the young birds I can still pull.* Whilst privately, he and I were away, admiring my glass slippers, away with the fairies, dancing in the glades, laughing and smiling, eyes only for each other (so I thought), twirling in the moonlight, pulling down the stars. We drank each other in through our eyes, stared and stared, imbibed and drank at the fountain of each other, as though we had never drunk before. And weightless too utterly without care, I swear we could have danced on dew-laden gossamer, espied on grass only in the dawn, without you noticing our passing. Like Cinderella and her Prince Charming, time carried us away. The future was rosy, glowing, the musicians in my head young, their bows pert.

Funnily enough – though I did not remark upon it at the time – we went our separate ways that night, in different taxis. The House was in session too, I saw the piece on it at the end of the 10 o'clock news. Presumably there she was, Mrs Bright Green Suit, captured within the House as the late-night sitting, not predominantly abolished until the early 2000s, went on. So where was he? It never occurred to me – wisdom not received, no slice even proffered to wonder. The naïve and foolish lover. Almost a title for a book. You would not believe it though. No one would. No one could have been that stupid, could they. I am not going to put a question mark to that last sentence. In my case, it is unaskable. Obsession, like alcoholism, can only be rectified by the person suffering it, acknowledging the problem. And there is no such thing as a wholly, utterly, totally reformed alcoholic.

Next day there was a picture of us – or rather, mainly of him – in the gossip column of the evening paper. He was named, Gerald Wendon-Davis, the husband of the Member for Norfolk North East, at a function for hale and hearties in the City. I wasn't. I have the cutting still, curled and brown with age. Under a ridiculous eighties haircut, all slicked back and up and sprayed into place, my head peering out between some outsize shoulder pads (which I might say the actresses from *Dallas* would not have been ashamed of), there I am. I have a sheepish look on my face, rather like the ewe who has not been told what the fox looks like. And grown up without ever seeing one, just like Little Red Riding Hood. Gerald looks like he is about to enjoy a good meal.

4

A Day at the Races

Lovers are never wholly relaxed: at sight of the other, your pulses race, your breathing quickens, there is an added sparkle to the eye. A blush comes over the cheek, altering the plane of the face, as it turns, like a sunflower to the path of the sun. And never more so, than in the youngest part of the relationship, when you are as a stream, you babble at each other with your sparkle and your limbs closely entwine, like the young stream as you breathe each other's exclusive, select atmosphere, twirl in the racing current together. Exclusive – it is only you two, how can anyone else possibly understand? Select, Gerald the Collector had selected me, for the glass cabinet. To collect. Little did I know, I was just another member of his seraglio. That realisation only came later. Downstream.

So when the white card invitation came, a day at Ascot, in a box, from Wendon-Davis Associates, well my heart leapt. A thick white card, italics. *Wendon-Davis Associates requests the pleasure of…* My name was written in black ink. Strong down strokes of the pen, more loops. Ascot. How exciting!

And Gerald! He had written: *Do hope you can make it!* 'Do' was underlined, very dark. How could I refuse? My heart was leaping like a March hare's.

True, it was not Ladies Day. When I had known Gerald longer, I learned whilst the Queen might go to Ladies Day, Mr and Mrs Wendon-Davis or even Mr Wendon-Davis without her, did not. They were somehow a breed apart. Mrs W-D did not like the antics of the other racegoers, dressed or undressed, on that particular day. Mr W-D probably did, the views at least, but did not attend… should I say, was not permitted to attend? Who knows?

It was a day towards the end of July. By that time, the Argentineans had surrendered on the Falklands, the task force was sailing home, the World Cup was over. It was a summer full of red, white and blue bunting – people were very gung-ho, following the example of the prime minister. The archbishop, a man of whom my mother could number herself one of his greatest fans, had just prayed at the memorial service for the dead of both sides, much to the annoyance of Mrs Thatcher, who had worn a most ridiculous straw boater, most unsuitable for her face and age. According to my mother who noted such things. This was, of course, long before the image-makers got at Mrs T's wardrobe and hair, long before the invention of that word, the makeover.

Back to the day at the races. What a delight! And with Gerald! In keeping with about a dozen others, as I discovered when I arrived. I had a big hat. Big hats hide discretions but in order to receive them, you have to allow people to come quite close. As Gerald did. As I entered the box, there he was, agreeing with the man next to him, "No, the Queen had not looked happy about Mrs T's attitude," which presumably referred to the memorial service about which there had been much backhanded commentary. Then, in the next breath as he looked up – his hand extended automatically, then, pausing to look at me properly – both hands came up in a businesslike embrace. "Hello," he cried in his big public I-am-jolly-pleased-to-see-you voice. And out loud: "How very nice to see you again, what a pleasure." All very businesslike. Except that when I leaned forward, he came under the brim of my hat and he whispered (I made him discreet, the hat caught the sound): "I shall crescendo with you and that hat before the day is over." And as he retreated, back out, from under the hat brim, so I caught the drift of his aftershave, saw the twinkle in his eye, had the sensation of his very smooth cheek against mine. And he turned to one of the men in the room, who was reaching forward to be introduced, shaking hands and said: "Couldn't you just admire a woman in a hat like that?" He winked at the man and twinkled at me. My heart was racing, reminded by the aftershave, the euphemisms, the Gerald-isms as clear as clear. He and I would come together again, press together, make love. Never mind where we were, I knew he would manage it. The first sip of champagne rocked my head, spun into my belly as a whirlpool. My breath had already shortened, just at the sight of him. My whole body was caught up, trapped, like a moth coming to the flame, unable to do anything else but dance. A fool's dance, the dance of the moth, ending only in tears. Or death.

This particular day at Ascot, there was a top libel lawyer, a couple of bankers, the managing director of a public-relations company, someone who was what they called then a captain of industry (as though industry were a ship, sailing charted waters), a criminal lawyer, a judge, one was a French man, others, I have forgotten. About five women amongst the dozen, all of them turning like flowers to Gerald's charm and his laughter and the hand on their waists. Did he know all of them that well? And to me, well, I was drawn in; no, that is not so, I was exhibited. I was Gerald's latest addition. Not exhibited in a sexual way, but more in the way of 'this is my latest discovery'. Did I feel patronised, was it sexist? I did not think so and now I can hardly remember. I can only now recall the anticipation, the sharpness of everything, of every gesture he made. My limbs hardly seemed to be mine, such was the longing in them for him. Was it now or would it be later, he would come for me? And where? It was, after all, a public racecourse.

I could hardly hear what people were saying, or hear it but not really comprehend. Round and round Gerald they danced, I danced. Years afterwards, it is dreadful, embarrassing to think of how one behaved, but I did. And is it really true, that your French improves with the more champagne you drink? Could I get away with the excuse, Gerald made me, drove me to being outrageous? It does not work for other people, why should it excuse me?

The day went on. Where the cobbler had sat up all night, making shoes for the fairies, so apparently I had stolen a pair. They were very high and made my ankles very chic. Or so I thought. I had tottered in them in the shop in front of a mirror. Naturally it was a new outfit, top to toe. It is not every day you get a white card invite to the races, to spend the day in a box, with Gerald Wendon-Davis. You can see how I was taken in. I danced in those fairy shoes and everyone knows you cannot rest till they rest. They will not rest, they will drive you, whip you, force you into a frenzy.

The day was a kaleidoscope of people and faces, and sound, laughter, all whirling, but always at the centre of it, the Lord of the Dance, Gerald, leading on, encouraging, coming back, calling the next step. And I danced, whirled, spiralled, on and on. Did I mention my hat was red? No one had warned me. "Red hat, no knickers?" asked the judge, grinning, thinking himself oh, so droll! How did he know? It was only later I realised it was a well-worn City slogan. "What a sweetheart," said the Frenchman in his beautiful, so-sexy accent. "You're a good-time girl," urged the banker. Blankly, I looked at him and danced on. "Come home with me," said the lawyer – the lawyer! By then I was past caring about his specialism. And the other four girls. Did they dance too?

About mid-afternoon, Gerald took me down to the paddock. I hardly remember the horses, all of them laboured long and hard over, honed to perfection for a fleeting few minutes on that day. I remember hats, binoculars, elegant men studying form, masses of beautiful women studying each other, but none so elegant of either sex, none to rival Gerald, who, putting his hand under my elbow, propelled me (how else?) to the ring side and muttered rude things to me, as he looked at the form. The dance did not stop. I was alight, afire with anticipation, ready to waltz amongst the stars again. How did I breathe, waiting for him to make the move, say 'Come with me' and we would couple, crescendo, somewhere despite the crowds? We would, we would, he had said. Pathetic now, looking back. Isn't it always so? Anticipation and Disappointment: lifelong twins.

But not then, no, then my heart was racing, I was aglow with pleasure, my skin tingling with expectation. We walked over with the crowds to the finish line, right down, literally feet from the line, in a concrete walkway in front of a wall and far below the level of the grandstands. The track was slightly above us. Was this… could this be the place? Might he even kiss me here? But how ridiculous even to think it, there were still masses of people around us. The crowd ebbed around us and settled. Someone said: "They're off." I was only aware of Gerald, his grey, grey eyes twinkling at me, the mole beside his eye riding the crinkles, rather like a small boat on a heavy sea. We lined up against the fence, my fingers clinging to the wire, he slightly behind me, his hand on my waist, proprietarily (the Collector or not to lose me?). I could feel his fingers, under my jacket, on my skin, against my rib cage. Could he feel my heart thumping, the breath shallow, the butterflies in my tummy?

Despite myself, I was diverted. I felt the ground begin to tremble. Far down the course there was a roaring. Louder, louder it came and with it a wind, and the earth began to shudder. The vibration began in the soles of my feet. Was the ground moving? Gerald moved closer, everyone went up on tip toe, heads craning, even me on those daft shoes. Everyone was taut, watching, yelling, yelling, exhorting. Come on, come on! There they were! Tiny figures, urging, urging, growing larger, the sound rushing towards us, the earth thundering, everyone screaming, names tumbling up into the air and all around us, the wave of sound up to us, above us, there they are! Then like a flash, a blur of pounding, masses of legs, a blaze of silks, a kingfisher dart of colour, they were past us, the soundwave over us and moving away, dying almost immediately, the ground stilled, everyone breathed out, relaxed. Ridiculously, I remembered then the only law of physics I ever learned, the movement of sound, and the momentum of movement, carrying the sound so quickly away. Then it was gone, and I was aware that Gerald had moved back, his fingers retrieved from my skin, as the crowd had fallen back from the rail. People were whooping around us. Several were smiling, elated at their luck. And I? I could still feel where he had been pressed against me, his hands on my skin; the excitement of the crowd taking their attention elsewhere. Gerald was still smiling, taking my elbow, drawing me away from the rail. The tide of horses for the next race was posed, waiting to begin in the paddock, even as the winners of the last race were collecting themselves to appear briefly, hotly, in the winner's enclosure, the owners to be congratulated, the jockey to be thanked, the punters to pick up their winnings. Surely it would not be much longer, surely he would take my hand, we would slip away, smile those secret smiles lovers smile only to each other; a different dance would begin to a different, more intimate, tempo?

But no, not yet. Gerald was an excellent host, indeed, apparently the consummate host. Past the paddock we went, where the next batch of horses was being viewed, back to the box, back to the whirl, the connections, the public dance. The lawyer was jubilant; he was up on the day. The public relations man was shaking his head at his losses, whilst one of the bankers smiled at me and said: "Come and dine with me tonight. I know a little place." I smiled, shaking my head, drunk on the heady combination of Gerald's touch, his proximity at the finish line, the anticipation of what was still to come; tonight was already taken, wasn't it? Gerald and I, we would go somewhere together, come together, crescendo. See, I was learning all his little terms.

And then to be so let down. When was he not there? When did he leave? How could the perfect host leave before his guests or, more to the point, without me? And unbelievably, it never occurred to me to ask when had he gone – I was too polite or too drunk – or with whom? That never occurred to me. Too innocent, too busy dancing to his tune. The piper had called it, then left the room. Gone. Gone, leaving the dance to finish without him. What is a tune without the piper? What was the day without Gerald? What was the point?

And then the awful bit, the public bit. I recall the shame of this, even now, the whole event, in its awfulness to be dredged up on the sandbank of memory at low tide. "Where's Gerald?" I wailed, in the first unstanched caterwaul, the grief of realisation, the tears rolling down my cheek, the onset of many through that night. The shame of it. Remember that moment in *My Fair Lady* at Ascot when the former flower girl urges on her horse as only she knows how. The swathe of gentility turns as one towards her. And so it was for me. The remainder of the box looked round, people in other boxes looked round. They pack the punters in so tightly there, to witness other people's misfortunes. Sobbing? I was inconsolable. "There, there," said the banker, producing what might have been once a clean handkerchief. Gerald's of course were always perfect, folded like a hospital bed's corner. I use this word often about him, but the handkerchiefs were always immaculate. Until given to me of course. And the banker actually said – in his then damp embarrassment, because I sobbed over him: "Don't take on so." He patted me. Even in my grief, I was careful to keep away from him.

Was this the high-water mark of my humiliation? No,

no there was worse to come. That high-water mark was far downstream, years away. This was just a ripple. Those accursed shoes. They were the last word in fashion. Still wailing, still tottering, I turned on them. Such ridiculous heels. And I fell. Fell headlong down the steps, from the balcony into the well of the main box.

The cobbler's magic broke. My glass flew out of my hand, my dignity collapsed, my skirt – not a particularly long one – rose. It was true what the judge had asked. There was my naked bottom on display for those looking to see. Whilst I had chosen to go knickerless, I fancied myself a stickler for detail in those days, my suspenders were red, matching the hat. And the shoes. The shoes that caused my downfall. The shame of it, the shame. But worse, still worse to come. Someone among those selected to be in the box, someone took a photo. This wasn't a matter of upskirting, no, this was the skirt, such as it was, had risen. Days later, my bottom was destined to be included in a photo-montage of views at Ascot. It was mine all right. Unnamed, it is true, but I know, I recognise the underwear, such as it is. The shame of it. It is thankfully true that you cannot see my face. Nor do I have any tattoos. I do, however, have a large mole on one buttock (of which Gerald grew very fond) and it is self-evident to me, even without the skimpy reference to underwear, whose buttocks they are. Besides, you can see the top of my stocking and a bit of the skirt. The raised skirt. Even now I blush at the thought. I have not kept this cutting, but it is burned into the memory, seared in, actually. This was long before that pair were photo-ed, grappling with each other in the most intimate way, at the winning post; was it only a couple of years ago, all over the front of the *Sun*? At the time, my photo… well, I hate to think of it as that, but it was scandalous. Afterwards, long afterwards, in an age less innocent, I did wonder was I set up? Was I tripped, was the photo taken – and I can remember the flash – to divert attention from Gerald's exit? Was I the scapegoat? Or is this all far too paranoid? Am I jumping at ghosts that are not there?

That day was privileged to be the first occasion – or rather the first known occasion – I was so let down; it was of course not the last. It was the start of the growth of the carapace I developed over the years. As had Mrs Wendon-Davis. Of course, I was let down dozens of times. Just like Mrs Wendon-Davis.

There is a tide in the affairs of men where, taken at the flood, the press may get the story. Years later, in late 1991, Gerald was caught in a coupling – that is to say, *in flagrante delicto* (as he might have said at another time, smacking his lips in expectation of the story, if it involved other people). Not with me, though, I had seen him on the Friday before. Most shocking of all was that it was the back of a car. Most un-Gerald-like; he usually liked his couplings in luxurious surroundings. Admittedly it was a Bentley. The *News of the World* exposed the story. It is one of several I collected in a book of cuttings from newspapers, which somehow over the years, quite unintentionally on each editor's part, tracks our relationship in print. I have never kept a diary; Gerald was dismissive of these: "A record of egoism," he would wave them aside, having seen too many publicised where the reverberations reacted badly and unexpectedly. In a sense, the press did the job for me, that and assiduous use of the scissors, cutting out the articles. For better, for worse. There is a school of thought that maintains 'keep a diary and one day it will keep you'. Increasingly from the mid-nineties, there became a stronger trend to publish diaries, spilling the beans on the life and times as the writer saw it or fashioned it. Many high-flying men in the world of politics or business were brought to earth by a Saturday-night phone call or the Sunday morning paper delivery full of revelations from their *bonking bimbos*, as one paper liked to call them. Mrs Thatcher's cabinets throughout the eighties were outstandingly consistent; consistent that is, in the number of men who maintained lovers, produced love children (my mother again, sniffily: *In my day, we called them bastards*), slept with underage persons of either sex or romped with prostitutes. Many, taking their ministerial roles as excuse or protection, flew like Icarus, fancying themselves immune from the normal moral structure of men, but crashing to earth with the delivery of those Sunday papers on the doormat, detailing all manner of proclivities, given by spurned lovers or those not paid enough to be silent. Some of those spilling the beans were Gerald's clients. Remarkably it never occurred to me to keep that diary and, after what happened at the end, well, it would have been impossible to publish, without invention. But I get far ahead of myself again.

Fortunately, on the occasion with the Bentley, there was not a photo of Gerald's buttocks, more of the pair – that is, he and she looking dishevelled leaving a party earlier that evening. Dishevelled? The always-so-elegant Gerald? With a young model, who clearly thought her star was in the ascendancy. She wanted to be an actress. Gerald was presumably on hand to provide the required uplift. More shocking too, even now, was that in the picture she has a tattoo on her shoulder. This was before tattoos became *de rigueur* in fashion terms in certain circles. From the photo, a little worn with age, a large strawberry may be seen on her left breast. It was a very large strawberry. Was this Gerald's latest concept of 'rough'? More interestingly, was it a deliberate 'exposure'? On her part or his?

That same Sunday afternoon, Gerald's name was splashed across the front pages, the Wendon-Davises called a press conference at the end of the drive. The farm drive, I noticed, not the main carriage entrance. Naturally I have never been to High Fold itself, but I can recognise a farm gate when I see one. The press pack had apparently travelled to north-east Norfolk – it was, after all, the weekend. Actually, Gerald had turned up there at dawn, passing those gentlemen of the press who had camped out all weekend, awaiting the story to blow. Mrs Gerald Wendon-Davis was in her constituency residency, doing good and great things. For the good and the great. The setting became the *à la mode* for straying Conservative politicians to emulate; Gerald, of course, had set the trend. The following year, David Mellor was one who followed the Wendon-Davis example, the chief difference being of course this time that it was Mrs Wendon-Davis who was the politician. Later variations of this scene were frowned upon by the Party; at least the Wendon-Davis marriage had no children to further besmirch the straying husband's reputation of using his family to keep his job afloat. Another difference between the 1991 version and Mr Mellor's was that I still have the strong suspicion that Gerald set the whole thing up for a publicity stunt, which worked too well and rather backfired on him.

However, there Gerald was, there was Mrs W-D, looking

remarkably drab, not the green suit that day. Perhaps it stayed in London. Presumably bright green was not appropriate in the circumstances, when your husband has been returned to you, having been caught in the act of cuckolding you, he all but fresh from his last well-publicised tryst. No green suit then but a grey twin set, a twin set, and pearls. Standing at the gate, keeping the press back. *I will stand by my man*, the headline thunders. They are holding hands. Remarkably, she has a handbag on her other arm, clamped into place. It is not clear if it is there for use as a weapon, if such were called upon, but if push came to shove, she was forearmed.

Frankly, I think the hand-holding is a bit much. She has a slab of lipstick, very pink, unbitten but stiff. It was not so very long after the papers moved to colour photos. Her hair is immaculate, lacquered, very blonde. Clearly it is something with which a simple thing like a breeze cannot meddle. But a spray can and bottle of dye has. She looks very ironed. Notice I do not say pressed. Pressed was our word – what he did to me – a Gerald-ism. He has a striped shirt on with a tie. Who comes down the drive, to stand by the gate, to meet the press in a tie? The farm gate, mind; it is after all only the fourth estate, the press. And a jacket, thrown apparently artlessly over the shoulder, like the clothes on a mannequin in a shop window. Nothing is careless or artless about Gerald. It is artlessly but carefully arranged. Gerald has clearly been mindful not to be sartorially challenged in such circumstances. Gerald has his I-am-a-jolly-nice-chap-really smile on. Clearly the hair has been recently coiffured. (Hair by the way is the same address as the nails – Jermyn Street – but a different timing to the appointment. Nails grow quicker than hair. Tony does the hair. Tony from Brighton.) Had

Tony been driven up from Jermyn Street specially? Secreted, like Gerald, past the waiting hordes? Or had she done it for him? It is not possible to see the nails. She has one lot firmly in her grip. Probably one of the rare times.

He watched himself on the early evening news. And rang. Of course I had watched it. No apology. Had he given Mrs W-D one? "Sweeting," he said with considerable *sang-froid*, "can't do lunch tomorrow. Got to go to earth for a day or so. Toe the line." He did not even bother to explain to me, assuming that I already knew what had happened, which of course I did. It would have been hard to miss it, unless I had spent the weekend on Mars.

On that occasion the press had a minor field day with him. News was very short at the time. I missed out on the lunch, though. Funny, on such occasions he acknowledged he knew where the line was. He crossed it with her, he crossed it with me. The girl he had been with sold her story to the *Sun*. Much of her was draped across its pages – with the strawberry tattoo taking centre stage – for much of the week. Monday's headline read *Gerald popped my cork in Bentley*. Where did that one come from? Hardly original on the part of the editor. Probably not good for selling Bentleys either. *Pick your own* was one of the minor exhortations above her picture on Tuesday. She was young and lithe and supple. Presumably she was also willing? The story did not say. Thursday's headline with the tattoo related to jam making. Much of the story was made up. It said Gerald liked bondage and being covered in shaving cream at crucial times. Bondage? Shaving cream? Gerald? I don't think so. Or only in Jermyn Street, whilst having the hair buffered and the scalp polished.

But again, I am jumping ahead. The day after that terrible

day at Ascot, he turned up at my flat. Should he have been in Norfolk? Where had he stayed that night? And with whom? But I never asked. How innocent is that? But then, young love is like that, you catch the current, go with the flow. Inexorably, each tide washes away the remains of the last. Love letters, names, warnings, pain – all written in the sand – are all gently erased by the incoming ripples of the next tide. And then, it was still very early in our relationship, I was not yet installed as the mistress, not yet had I learned the art of ranting and how it was so otiose (a Gerald-ism).

That morning, I was nursing a hangover. Overnight, my head had split in two. I knew how Humpty Dumpty felt. It was about half past ten and there was, thankfully, a pot of coffee on. My clothes were in a pile near the front door, where I had stepped out of them the night before. The cobbler's workmanship, the fairy shoes were discarded in a corner. I never wore them again. My feet were a throbbing mass, my toes a collection of white, bloodless worms. My elbows and my side hurt from where I had hit the floor. I could only hobble and that with some difficulty. Stepping over the clothes and moving them with my foot to one side, I opened the door to him.

Letting him in, so *soigné* for that hour in the morning, a truly remarkable attribute given how he had spent the previous day and presumably had spent the night, I looked in the mirror. ("Have a mirror near the door, dear," one of my mother's strictures. "You can check on yourself before you leave." If only I had not listened to her.) There I was, caught, snared, snagged in the reflection. *Dear God,* I thought, *the hair has gone into serious overdrive.* A distant part of me noticed it was becoming a very Gothic-looking bird's nest

– a rigid bird's nest – after the rigours of the day before. At any moment something in feathers might alight upon it and set up home. And the lipstick was very dark and the eye make-up very heavy. I was in the process of preparing a face swollen with tears from the night before, for the day ahead. A new one might have helped. There are some things make-up cannot help you with.

Looking again, I could see that there were serious shadows under the heavily lined eyes and I was 'glowing' slightly (Gerald: *Only horses sweat*) from the excesses of the previous day's (and much of a late and solitary night's) alcohol. I was a crumpled disaster zone – one where the debris was apparently still falling – and never more so than in comparison to this vision I had just opened the door to, who wore a perfectly ironed, open-neck shirt and looked rather like a Ralph Lauren model, just new out of the hay, so to speak, perfectly dressed, freshly scented, coiffured, manicured. An entirely crease-free, utterly scented and cool, stress-resistant zone.

But he made nothing of it. He came in. Swift, unconscious glance at his own reflection. Sartorial Assessment: perfect. In a stride he was over the discarded shoes, bounding past the untouched *Sunday Times*, still lying where it fell on the floor, with a picture of the newborn Prince William and his mother on the front. After this particular weekend, the paper boy would curse me, as we would have had every Sunday paper delivered, to assuage Gerald's need for successful stories about his ascending stars, as he liked to call them. That would be in the future though.

For now, he stepped over my clothes as though it was perfectly normal to do so (Nanny would have suffered a heart attack at the sight of them – if Gerald's own measured undressing, folding and putting away was anything to go by. Even in the height of his passion). He was carrying flowers. See how hungover I was, that I only noticed then. It was a huge bouquet. Like a sort of trophy. Beware, as you fall in the chasm, of the man carrying flowers. There should be a government warning, if not an outright ban. Especially heavily scented ones if you are still feeling sick from the day's alcohol and the night's further alcohol. I remember bracing my rebelling stomach against the stench of perfumed flowers.

"Sweeting darling," he cried. Through the alcohol-induced haze, I could hear my mother saying "She does have a Christian name" through clenched teeth, but my mother was not there, Gerald could not hear her, and he never called me it, only wrote it in those letters Mrs W-D might attempt to vet, if she had a mind to. "Darling, look at you, what have you done?" Notice, not *What have I done to you? Ripped your heart out, jumped on it a few times, minced it, set fire to it and shovelled the remains down a nearby handy drain. Spent the night with another woman I forced you to meet yesterday and be nice to. Even though I could see you hated each other. And then I went away with her, crushing your ego underfoot, unregarded. Never even said goodbye to you. Spent the night with her. And jolly nice it was too.* No? No, none of that.

"Let me help you, darling," (he was always offering help) and so saying, he wrapped me in a huge embrace, with the flowers. "These are for you," and there was such a scent of crushed blossoms. Was this not a heady enterprise? Can you not see how I lost my brains? How was I not sick on him? And the flowers...? Well, of course, I took them from him, as petals dripped from them, over the carpet, like drops of… well, blood. It came to me, as clear as day even through my sodden and befuddled haze, the memory of a woman in my office, only earlier that week who had received flowers. I did not, as she had, take them carefully from the delivering florist, put them on the floor, a dozen long-stem red roses in her case, place them carefully as though she was utterly mindful of their delicacy. The woman – a tall, elegant woman, never one to seem flustered – then moved as though to step over them, but instead brought her high and pointed heel down, deliberately over and over, without any sound from her and crushed each rose head in turn into the carpet, so that the floor flecked with red, blood red, the pieces of petal eventually spattered into the far corners of the room. It was only then, as she turned her back on the carnage, that I noticed her red-rimmed eyes and later that I learned that her husband had been someone else's lover too and, in so doing, had fathered a son on this other woman who collected other women's men. Mine were not roses. It did not occur to me to trample upon them.

But back to the scene in hand! We embraced, Gerald still holding the flowers. The flowers were retrieved, some crushed, ruined. There were some petals still falling to the floor in the mêlée. Is there a metaphor there – should I have seen it? But no matter, in due time he arranged them (my mother: *Never trust a man who can arrange flowers*; but she was not there, he couldn't hear her), he arranged me, he produced champagne, hair of the dog, and the world was suddenly a-sparkle afresh, he was walking on water and I was, well, I was thistle down, toes and hangover forgotten, adrift on the breeze of his aftershave, the crushed lavender well to the fore, capable of a sexual marathon Catherine the Great would have been proud of. There, I have brought it down to earth again. Bump. There is no romance in the act of sex, whatever Gerald wanted to have me call it. True, there are no lies, not in the act itself, which should be warm and pleasurable, and above all, if nothing else, loving then. Cynicism and much pain should be kept away until afterwards.

Have you heard this before? The end of the afternoon, eggs, a light supper. Cooked to perfection, and Gerald actually whipped them (*Mother!* But she wasn't there and had no *bon mot* to add) into a frenzy of air. I say nothing here, except they were the most wonderful eggs and, of course, then, yes, then I was in love. Of course they would be wonderful. Eggs sour on you if left too long and too many clog your system. Old ones, if broken, stink. I was too young to see any of that.

5

A Visit to the Tailor

I remember one day we went to the tailor's together. Gerald's suits were works of art. Whatever happened to his body, whatever time did to it, his suits covered a mass of errors and weaknesses, making the outer view elegant, even, dare I say manicured, in much the same way a gardener manicures a garden. Tidy a rose here, prune a hedge and the overall effect is much greater than the sum of the parts. Much of the suits were still hand-stitched and the linings were individual but not gaudy, as later became a fashion in the City in the nineties.

Gerald's tailor. His father's before him. And grandfather's before him. The family tailor then was located in Savile Row, or just off it. I must have known Gerald quite well by then or was it just a chance meeting in the street and a wave of the hand and Gerald all full of bonhomie, a hand to my elbow, a circling arm behind it and a sweeping off the feet, accompanied by the imperious command, "Come to my tailor's and then we can do a spot of lunch"? See, this is not important but how could you refuse? Imagine it, Gerald hailing me from across the road, crossing, traffic lurching to accommodate his passage, the big hello, the huge embrace, the scent engulfing the last of the senses as you succumb to his urging. "Come on, Sweet, do come. I shall only be five minutes, then we can have a bit of something. Do come, oh say you will." Is that how it was? Can't remember. My memory has honed the details down to the very specific.

Even now, I wonder what sort of a man takes a woman with them to the tailor? Gerald's is a private sort of a place, much is made of curtains, screening the client from the world as his most intimate details are recorded, screening the client from the lowly servants who are involved in the construction of his new clothes. Everything is sleek, polished, beeswaxed, oak-panelled drawers, there since the Ark; everyone smiles. Tugging the forelock has gone but everyone bows ever so slightly over shaking the client's hand: "Can remember your father, your grandfather, sir." Certainly they knew Gerald. Mr Gerald, to distinguish him from his forebearers of the family name.

I was introduced, airily, a wave of Gerald's manicured hand. Seeing it now, I would recognise a certain smile between men, I the latest, one of a string, like a racehorse, but I was not to know that then, the tailors were all very discreet. It is a training that goes with the territory; like the hairdresser, there are few occupations more circumspect than the tailor. Discreet fussing, rather as tailors do when a client has put on weight. No reference is made to increased inches or a spreading waistline. Here again, the client is screened from such news. Within the confines of the curtains where the tailor and client conspire together, the measurements are never specifically named. More the tailor will say something like, *Perhaps it would be more comfortable if we were a bit more generous here? Or allowed a bit more there?* The client is not told his measurements. Or that they have expanded. A woman guards hers more closely than her jewels. Jewels can be made public, measurements never spoken of. She worries over them, lies over them, keeps them more secret even than her sexual escapades. A woman's measurements, in every sense of the word, go to the grave with her. A man does not know his measurements, never remembers them and could not care less.

I was shown to a chair. Clearly it would never do to leave a woman untethered in the tailor's – rather like leaving a loud child unmonitored in the library. Who knows what havoc may be committed! The tailor and Gerald disappeared into the series of Arabian curtained tents at one end of the room. I could hear faint mutterings as the tailor whispered figures to his attendant who wrote things down or more loudly, "I suggest the cavalry twill, sir," as the tailor spoke to Mr Gerald. Gerald was clearly not inhibited by the quiet, broken only by the ticking of an ancient but highly polished clock and the muted roar of traffic that serves as the constant backdrop to London.

The tailor had gone; Gerald's head came through the curtain. By then I was mooching about looking at different cloths. He hissed: "How about it, Sweeting? A quick aperitif?" I just gaped. "Come on," he urged, "we haven't got long." What came over me? How did my feet move? Would you believe that I, an otherwise perfectly normal, quite sensible – staid even – voting, taxpaying, law-abiding citizen… would you believe that I went to him? A quick aperitif? Not to put too fine a point on it, he was inside me – I was clamped onto him

– before you could say 'Smoked salmon canapé madam?' or 'Would you like ice with that?' He had what you might call a robust appetite. 'Up for it' became the term for his readiness. As for me, well, I was younger then, more receptive…

He was going like a train. I shall not record too many more of the details here. Suffice to say, yes, another ripple, well a tidal wave actually on the rising tide of humiliation, yes, after a bit the tailor came back. Gerald had just finished. He had just about removed himself. Don't ask me about stains, scent, about noise, about any of it. The tailor's footsteps came towards us – how is it I did not register what these were? The tailor's hand came to the curtain; the tailor's head came through the curtain. All, as they used to say at harvest time, was gathered in or taken in (it was, after all, the tailor's), all recorded, digested. Returned to earth with the most awful crash, all I wanted to do was cover my face, dig a huge hole, crawl into it, die. Is this what they do to racehorses who cannot stand again after a jump? The utter humiliation. Gerald meantime had zipped himself up, the tailor had retreated, coughed – as tailors and solicitors and doctors and others who 'do', do at such times – and Gerald, fully recovered, fully in charge, shook his mane (here I am tempted to write 'and roared' but much as I would like to pretend otherwise, he did not) and called out to the tailor, who was Mr George.

"Mr George, now then, about that grey cloth." Mr George came in. Can you believe this? The tailoring went on, as though nothing had happened. Nothing was said. There was, however, much mutual clearing of the throat, a competition between Gerald and Mr George. Now I wonder: were they fighting back the giggles?

It was about this time that Gerald took to wearing glasses. Not, you understand, for everything. "No, no," he would wave them about, "just for reading the small print." The glasses, believe it or not, on a peacock so fine were very similar to those black, rather square-rimmed frames 'sported' (a Gerald-ism for the wearing of glasses) by Michael Caine in the film *The Ipcress File*. Gerald liked to rerun that scene where Caine as Harry Palmer is asked by the beautiful actress, after he has cooked her dinner: "Tell me, do you always wear those glasses?"

"Always," says Harry, "except in bed." Gerald would wink, as he completed the story. "Then she reaches for the glasses." There was no demeaning thing like someone else's name on them – which became so popular in the nineties, no, there was just a raised, embossed *G* on each side of them. Not for Gucci, that came later. Just *G*. Not painted, just proud of the frame, so that you knew they were made specially. For one man.

The glasses were no help on this occasion. Worse was to befall us. To say that Gerald brought the curtain down on his performance that day would not be a falsehood. He lifted his foot to adjust his trouser leg and in putting the heel of his shoe down, misjudged the distance and caught the hem of the curtain. There was a crack and then a clang as the metal bar holding the curtain left its moorings in the ceiling, then a *whoosh* as the whole enclosure of material that had afforded us not a jot of true privacy, crashed to the floor around us, leaving us swathed in a sea of curtains. I was horrified. Fortunately, by then Gerald was dressed, but for his jacket, which he calmly slid on. What more could befall us? Gerald, utterly composed as though curtains crashing were an everyday occurrence, turned to me with a smile, took my hand as though he were a prince about to rescue me from a fate worse than death – which I was beginning to think it was – and guided me over the foaming mass of material. There was such a twinkle in his eye. *Beware the man* – too late for that, far too late.

Mr George smoothed his features out of a smirk and into a smile, rather as a hand moves over a piece of cloth, easing out a crease. There was a lot of coughing in the background and clearing of the assembled tailors' throats, rather like a group of frogs' chorus, then much bowing and scraping, as though Gerald had somehow done them a favour. Only I noticed the wink between Gerald and Mr George. No money exchanged hands for the damage but some very good tickets for one of Gerald's theatrical connections – theatrical in the more orthodox sense here, involving a stage and actors rather than Gerald's antics – were pressed upon Mr George in a flourish of Gerald's finely manicured hands. As we left, Gerald was urging him to bring Mrs George to the production (for presumably there was one, since *& Son* was included in the name of Gerald's tailor) and Mr George was bowing over the open door as Gerald swept me through it.

Propelled (though now I was getting wise to this), into a small and select restaurant just nearby, the usual story, the *maître d'*, the fuss, the chilled glass of white wine (how did Gerald always manage to do this?), my head in my other hand (the shame of it all, the shame!), Gerald held court over the small circular table, looking at me over his glasses which he had rakishly pulled down his nose, looking at the white, crisp tablecloth, the flowers, the tailored and folded napkins, the crystal glasses waiting for his second order. Someone in the corner was plucking at the strings of a harp. The world seemed quite normal, ordinary. I was still in shock. Had I just simply imagined it? And Gerald laughed, well, on this occasion chuckled. He actually chuckled. "Worry not, my little Sweeting," said he between chuckles, patting my hand. As you do to someone in shock. "Mr George has seen worse, far worse in his day." And he winked broadly. Who cared about Mr George – what about me? For shame, for shame. How could I have allowed myself?

And what about the curtains? Now, looking back I wonder was that one of Gerald's little diversions? Forever after, even mention of the curtains crashing to the floor could reduce Gerald into a shuddering, giggling mass, though you would never have known at the time. "Sweeting, my lovely," he would gasp between guffaws, "if you could have seen your face! Amid all that cloth. Venus rising from the foam could not have looked more coy!"

Gerald had been circumcised. I presumed he was Jewish. An early example of tailoring? Once, on a sunny afternoon – post-coupling, sorry coming together and Gerald was not in a rush – I asked in all innocence which bit of Wendon-Davis had been anglicised. "Jewish?" he queried. "No, no, I had the job done at the request of Mrs W-D." There she was, between us, in the bed, an unbidden, unwelcome, unwanted spectre. In the House in the bright-green suit, but also, cloned green suit and all the money, with us. He turned and put his hands behind his head, to lie back and contemplate the ceiling. "No, no my lovely, she had the specification, I measured up to it, I wanted her lovelies, so I had the op."

Smiling to himself, he contemplated the ceiling further.

"She wanted me," he said, clearly still amazed at such good taste on the part of his wife. "I suppose," he mused, "choosing a partner is rather like buying a house. You see it, and you change it to how you want it, modify it, put an extension in, paint it, that sort of thing." I was surprised. At that point, Gerald had never had to buy a house in his life, let alone do anything to it; High Fold had come with Mrs W-D and presumably there were an army of 'doers' involved in its upkeep. He had had the op; her side of the bargain was High Fold and, well, I did not want to know what else she had brought to the marital bed. Clearly a great deal of money. Even so, circumcision was hardly the same as having an extension put on the side of your house. Rather the opposite might be true, or so I would imagine.

He was following a train of thought. "Yes," he mused. "I wanted her lovelies. And what a lot of lovelies there were." I have said that lovelies, in Gerald-language, was money, mostly his wife's. Clearly, the tailoring operation had been worth it. "I could spend it then, currency," he said. Making a passing reference to my breasts with his hands, he said casually but unsubtly, like a bad radio link: "These are lovelies, but only I can spend them. Not much use to you, really." Jokes were not really in Gerald's list of talents. Was I disgusted? Was it belittling for a man to physically alter himself, to please his wife? No, I can't say that… to capture his wife? Or rather, her money? Is that the ultimate in tailoring for men: first the clothes, the hair, then by steps, the nails, the body? But isn't that what a woman does, with tissues in her bra, then pads and, finally, implants? Is it somehow more degrading in a man, or am I – cynical I – being sexist as well as appalled? Was it any more degrading than all the other things he did?

Had Mrs W-D taken the full measure of him, his extramarital habits, and decided to let sleeping dogs lie? If, for example, she murdered him because of me, and all the others, would it come out, that he had had the operation at her request? The press does discover the strangest things when people die or are killed. Was that request so awful? But this is running ahead. She would never think to murder him. Presumably it would not wash with the other members of the Green Suit Brigade. There were a number of them in the House that summer, shades of green – and shades of orange and pink, but all part of the same party, the same crowding round the television screen for the voting public to consume. Would it have washed with the voting public? Okay for a woman to change herself for a man, but the other way round? And in the constituency of Norfolk North East, how would that go down with the blue-rinsers? And murder? Even if he did cuckold her on every occasion – never!

As for the coupling at the tailors, humiliating as it was, I learned afterwards this was Gerald's then-current idea of al fresco or a bit of rough. The tailor even caught Gerald dabbing at me with his handkerchief, hospital corners to the fore, so to speak.

Looking back, Gerald was always dabbing at me, whether it was blood or semen, or something more publicly acceptable, such as wine. As ever, he was immaculate, never mind he had just achieved orgasm – or in Gerald-ese, crescendo – in amongst the tailor's curtains. The hair was immaculate, nothing ruffled, nothing had moved. I cannot remember now if he sprayed it. What a thought. Perhaps Tony had induced him to, Tony in Jermyn Street, Tony from

Brighton. He minced. Sometimes, if Gerald was in a good mood, he could mince like Tony.

Tony was discreet, more so than Gerald. It goes with the territory, like Mr George's. Tony knew about Gerald's bald patch under the mane and covered it professionally. Gerald would dab at that too. After one particularly humiliating interlude, I put hair remover in the shampoo in Gerald's overnight bag. He liked to be immaculate, which included the elegant and elegantly managed coiffeur of the great mane. I did not see him for some time after that. But the evening papers for the night but one after that reported sighting the husband for the Member for Norfolk North East, in a hat. In the middle of August! It is true it was the silly season. But such a hat! I have the article and the picture. Gerald in a black hat, still elegant, rakish even. Of course, the hat is at an angle. The camera has caught the top of his high cheekbone and traces the headland of the bone as it begins to curve down towards his mouth. It is a good picture, still the twinkle in his eye, his smile racy, apart from an extra chin. And shortly after that, the same paper reported his shorter hairstyle, making no reference to the bald patch I had only worked on to enlarge. *Is the lovely Gerald seeing someone new?* wondered the gossip columnist in the paper, remarkable in an age, where people do not wonder such things in print, when the person being wondered about is married to the Member for the Bright Green Suit. More to the point, did they know something I did not? Was the someone me? Or someone else? As the creator of the new *Style*, (Gerald-ese) for such it was, Tony got the credit. I got nothing, not even a byline.

6

A Public Meeting

Over the years that I knew him, Gerald had a series of cars, large ones with air conditioning, and cocktail cabinets and leather seats (not cream, "Stains too easily, eh, Sweet!" Gerald would say with a wink). He liked to drive himself, in large, comfortable, well-built and expensive cars. Gerald did not 'do' public transport. Certainly, in London he never travelled by Underground. "Transit of the masses, for the masses," he would proclaim, as if the masses had some choice in the matter. "All done on the cheap," he pronounced on more than one occasion, turning his eyes to me to see if I was looking. One of Gerald's favourite maxims would be coming, I could tell. He would draw himself up, still checking with half an eye that I was watching: "The bitterness of poor quality lasts long after the sweetness of low prices!" he exclaimed. "But it certainly is not cheap." I could only protest on deaf ears. He had spoken. To Gerald, the Underground was anathema, probably in fact, one of the few things he hated about London.

Sometimes, Gerald had a chauffeur. Fred was one of them. Fred was not really a Gerald sort of person and thus very often at that time Gerald drove himself. Fred was there for the Wendon-Davises to be ferried around London and up to Norfolk. I think though, that Gerald felt Fred grew to know rather too much and so Fred was only assigned mostly to those more orthodox journeys that Gerald made. Fred was part of the army of 'doers' associated with High Fold. Gerald liked to call Fred "Mr Frederick" or eventually Mr Fred. It was better for the Wendon-Davis image. Later, having left the Wendon-Davis employ, Fred tried to sell his story. Gerald did not think highly of this. In one of his letters to me at the time, Gerald wrote:

> *He has a death wish, that is, I wish him dead. Unpleasantly so. To say that he is gormless is an injustice to gorms rather as calling some humans 'pigs' is a disservice to pigs who are actually quite friendly and, on occasion, civilised animals. He has started on a long and arduous path of pain and retribution, though he does not know this yet. I will have my revenge upon him. Nasty man. He is also the one – I think I may have told you about – who has just discovered, six months after the birth, that he is the father of a six-month-old baby girl by one of his ex-girlfriends. This adds, in parenting terms, or sperm donation at least, to the boy in Norwich (age unknown) and two teenage boys who live with him in a village near High Fold. Needless to say, all have different mothers, legal status unknown but suspected.*

A judiciously timed injunction put the stop on Mr Fred's intended sale. It would not be the last. "Heeee is, how you say, a scorpion without zee sting," cried Gerald, pretending to be foreign, disclaiming as usual, when he told me the news. He puffed up and down my kitchen, or rather he puffed in the small space that passes for my kitchen. He had heard the phrase on the radio, about a politician who had done little for his constituents and the phrase had stuck in his magpie-like mind. He had, as usual, collected it for use later.

Fred was replaced by a friend of Tony's. Marcus, who also came from Brighton, wore particularly strong aftershave. I did wonder if this might drive Gerald underground, leaving the car at home, but upon such a suggestion he would mutter again, "Transit of the masses," and hear no more on the matter. Marcus, like Tony, was discreet. Perhaps it had something to do with Brighton. In the end, Marcus moderated his scent.

I often thought of Gerald's comments when stuck underground. Londoners like to think of themselves as a breed apart, a cut above the rest of the country. But down there, underground – in the dark, the rats and the dirt – all Londoners are equal and none are as equal as their bovine counterparts, the more well-known occupants of the cattle truck that at least have EU regulations to protect their valuable carcasses and the space required for cows to occupy. On the Underground, there is something so debasing about the crush, the sharing of the most personal space, the intermingling of breathing such restricted and recycled air, the clash of morning-fresh perfume with your neighbour's breath carrying the last vestiges of yesterday evening's dinner, the overwhelming heat, the dirt, the utter, utter intimacy in a place where you do not want intimacy with complete strangers. Perhaps to be truly a Londoner, you have to become inured to such invasion, such a reduction to the common denominator of the sheer hell of getting to work. Stoically, you subsume into the masses of bodies and pick up your personal space, your individuality, as you leave the train at journey's end. And everyone had a bag, or two bags, supermarket bags, expensive leather briefcases, rucksacks, handbags, sometimes (to be dreaded in the rush hour) suitcases. No one gets on a train without at least one bag. No wonder Gerald always wanted to rush to help me. "Come to me ye who are heavily laden," I would mutter, seeing another person forcing their bag before them into the confined space of the carriage, before pressing their bodies after it. And small wonder the rest of the country laughs as they journey to work along country roads, or cycle or walk to their places of travail. And in minutes, not hours.

It was a Tuesday and I had been called to a meeting in London. At the time I had a flat outside the centre of town. This particular morning, January 1986, the papers were full with all the aftermath of the Westland affair crashing around the Cabinet's ears and still over every paper's front page, who had promised what to whom. Michael Heseltine had just resigned and there was much speculation over who was going to resign next. All of these machinations were at that point immaterial to me that morning; it was very cold, demanding warm clothes. I dressed accordingly.

Being thoroughly bundled up, I got to the Tube at Leyton and found, amid the heaving crowds, that the Central Line – that lifeblood of the whole Underground system – was not working. In true traveller fashion, undeterred, I fought my way up the station steps and patiently waited (Gerald did not 'wait', or for that matter, 'queue'). I was made of stern stuff in those days, where travelling across London was concerned.

Eventually, I managed to find a space on the fourth train that came in. Off went the train ultra-slowly. I was up against the Westland story then, as people around me tried to read their papers, failing badly with the movement of the train and the crush. And as we travelled down the line, underground, so we began to pick up more and more people, so that from my tiny position by the door (as it was impossible to get a seat even when the line was running properly) I was jostled into the corner and more and more crushed. Before the second station had passed (there were seven in my journey then. If possible on a good day, I would shut my eyes against the human hell in the carriage and count the stops), I began to become aware of a chap standing facing me – well, more like face to face with me – who had a persistent cough. Which to be fair, he was trying to divert away from me (rather difficult given the space allowed) but by doing so, the arm that he was hanging/holding onto the strap with was threatening to decapitate – if not seriously de-hair – the girl who was standing next to me. Standing next to me? No, she was virtually standing on me. The train stopped. It was between tunnels. Time passed. There was a lot of coughing. Did he spit on me?

There were several people listening to music. Or rather, we were all listening to one person's music, which he had pumped directly into his ears but at a level he was apparently willing to share with all of us. It was not something worthy of being shared, or indeed, welcome. I wondered if the cattle have such problems on their trains.

After a while the train started again. Ever the optimistic – after all, I had managed to get on the train – I looked round for something to divert me from the rising heat and general discomfort. At such times, I try to believe that there is always something. And so there was. Seated about six feet away (and I could see her clearly from my crushed position by the corner window) was a girl applying make-up. Not any ordinary girl, but the girl I quickly realised Gerald had gone off with that day at Ascot. That terrible, terrible day, what, some three years previously.

Now it is hard to believe, but by the time we reached Liverpool Street in the City – say eight minutes from the stop before it on a normal day, perhaps twenty-five on this one – she had applied mascara (several times) to two eyes. The time it was taking, I wondered if she had more. Then lipstick. And this was true – I saw it – three lots of lipstick, different ones, to her lips. I was tempted to see if they were larger lips than the norm but no, not abnormally so. Over them she went, and over and over and over. I began to wonder if there was something strange about them – the lips – when eventually, at least ten or fifteen minutes later, she stopped and apparently the lips passed muster. Frankly, I would have thought with the shine on them, you could have directed planes to Heathrow on a cloudy night, but then who was I to judge? And remember the pain she had caused me. Albeit unwittingly. I felt my cattiness was at the very least her just deserts. For her, though, there was worse to come.

I muttered to the girl standing on me: "I wonder what she is going to put on next." But apparently the process was over. Now fully made-up, the Ascot Girl (I can't remember her name now but this would do, being similar to a Geraldism, he made up names for everyone) crossed her nails, sorry, fingers that had very specific and defined nails, with very dark red polish (matching the lips but numbers of coats and colours unknown) and resigned herself to the journey. A distant part of my mind wondered if she had marked Gerald's skin with those nails that night after Ascot, but then no, I had seen him the following day. Hadn't I. How foolish. Looking back now, why hadn't I just shut the door in his face that morning?

Eventually, amid much heat and discomfort, more music – or rather the boom, boom, boom of the by now presumably deaf young man nearby – we arrived at St Paul's. Crumpled, creased, very hot, itchy with the heat from a by then completely redundant winter coat, the water running down my spine, I managed to force a way off the train and pull my bag to me, from between the bodies still in the carriage, pressed sardine-like against each other. And so did the girl from Ascot. Who had danced that now long-ago summer's day to Gerald's tune so completely. And won the prize.

She did not see me – or indeed acknowledge me – but we were close going up the escalator; she was slightly in front of me. It had been some three and a half years since we last met. Given the opportunity would I have acknowledged her? Up we went, preparing ourselves for the day again (though she had already done the job on her face), smoothing ourselves down, mopping the heat off after the cattle truck ride now behind us. As we came over the bend of the escalator to the fresher air, imagine my surprise – and it was real surprise – for there, standing at the barrier, was Gerald. Gerald. My breath deserted me at the very sight of him. Sweet, lovely, immaculate, elegant Gerald. Crisp, white shirt, beautiful suit, peacock Gerald. And a huge bouquet, just huge. My lips began to tug into a smile (remember, I was relatively newly in love still).

But something tempered my enthusiasm. What was

Gerald doing there, who was he waiting for? Her? Would this hurt me afresh? Remember that awful, desperate night, when I sobbed my heart out for a man who had gone away, promising so much, leaving nothing, no goodbye, no nothing, with another girl. The girl now just ahead of me. We at the end of the twentieth century in the West did not train our sisters and daughters to accept the rules of the harem. Nor yet at the start of the twenty-first century. Perhaps I should have learned. Perhaps it would have lessened my pain. Doubtless, readers of the *Guardian* Women's page will shudder at such comments. Certainly my mother would have done. And hung her head in shame at the actions of her daughter.

All of this thought in a second, I stopped at the top of the escalator. How was it no one could hear my heartbeat? All other sound seemed to vanish. My mouth went dry. An ache started in my tummy. There was Gerald at the barrier, the girl saw him and hesitated. Gerald with flowers, obviously waiting for someone. My heart was booming. Could no one else hear it? She hesitated, his eyes brushed over her, came back, half-smiled, but I could see he only registered a pretty (if heavily made-up) girl, not someone he had spent an evening (if not the night) with, after a day racing. Nearly three years previously. And who knows what else? His eyes, hardly acknowledging her, turned away from her. A cynic might add, there had been so many other one-night stands since then, with so many other women, but not I, not that day at least.

What a terrible put-down. Perhaps I even gasped in shock. More controlled than I would have been, she settled her shoulders, walked on, back straight. Gerald's antics had that same effect on Mrs W-D, straightening her spine. The

Ascot Girl did not stop and make conversation, seeing, in a second, how the land lay. She walked on, up the stairs, and disappeared. What a price she must have paid; what a terrible price. I knew her heart was breaking, for shame, if nothing else. Believe me I knew – I had been there. But that was not mine to dwell on. It was not a moment to cherish, to have my revenge. Oddly, I really felt for her, sharing a common sisterhood (shades of the harem) and that common heartbreak. But there was no time to consider this. It was impossible for me to delay any longer and I walked forward.

"Sweeting," he boomed, with his huge smile. I just know everyone looked round. So did he. In some small back corner of my mind I even hoped upon hope Ascot Girl was out of range. How very embarrassing. "What a pleasure!" and laughing, he opened his arms. "I have been waiting for you." Then, imagine it, what a joy, what a welcome. For me! He had been waiting for me! Now, to my older mind, to my more tutored cynicism, was this true, did he look, for a split, split second, over my shoulder? Was there someone else he was actually waiting for? He could hardly overlook two of the harem, within seconds of each other. Could he?

"Sweeting, Sweeting, my lovely," he boomed, chuckling at my confusion, knowing he was making a scene, gathering me to him, to the watchers, friends warmly greeting each other. "Great news, clever Gerald, big deal. Come and join me for a cup of coffee, bit early for bubbly." Note not clever old Gerald. Anyone else would say 'old' but not Gerald. Gerald would never admit to age, in any formal fashion.

On he sped, full of excitement, the words tumbling out, to tell me his news. "Oh, and these are for you," almost as an afterthought, as though it was obvious, pressing the flowers to me. Why else would he be carrying flowers at that hour in the morning? For my part, I was still so hot, crumpled, flustered. See, still I did not register the warning: beware the man carrying flowers – my mother would throw up her hands at me. "What does he want?" she would question, suspiciously, screwing up her eyes in her cynicism. By complete contrast to my state, he of course was cool, crisp, elegant... so very elegant. The chin had still not yet begun the major slide – but I get ahead of myself again. He took me by the hand – with his spare, manicured, smooth, perfect hand – and tugged me – well, of course he did not really tug – to a coffee house, all fresh after early morning preparations for the day.

What a delight, Gerald, seeking me out (I still never asked how he knew where I was), seemingly buying a florist's whole shop of flowers; it was such a large bouquet, all for me. It was for me, wasn't it? And then telling me his news, as though it was vital I knew. A good scandal – Gerald's goods in trade, so to speak – is like a fine wine. The groundwork needs to be prepared, the bottle corked and stored correctly, turned at intervals. When coming to be drunk, you should choose your imbiber as carefully as you might a lover – the wine should be appreciated appropriately, as should the scandal. The wine, like the scandal, has a bouquet, something to be sniffed over, salivated, mulled upon, the taste hinted at. And then poured into the glass, rolled around the tongue before the final denouement, the drinking. And the spitting out. All this Gerald had done, with some wannabe and some declining star, in conjunction with his chosen gossip page. It was big news in their world, big news to the outside world. Gerald was cock-a-hoop. He would be the name behind the headline that lunchtime. Already the wider press would be gathering. We did not have much time; he was even then en route to one of the London radio stations. And in the midst of all this, he wanted to impart it all to me – had troubled to seek me out, to wait. Is this not heady, is this not magical? Would you, could you have kept your feet on the floor with such attention? Regardless of the story, the reason, would you not be lost in a spiral of stars and music and twinkling bits, and all those magical things the princess has in fairy tales after the prince has kissed her? And never, never a thought for the girl – slept with, left behind, overlooked – who had gone her way with a broken heart, unrecognised, perhaps even forgotten, by Gerald, seen waiting for someone else at the barrier. Not a thought then.

Imagine then, returning to earth from this dance along the Milky Way; I was going to a meeting, how was I going to explain a florist's entire shop in my arms? What was I going to do with it? But Gerald did not think of such things; it was the instance that counted, not what happened afterwards. The meeting at the barrier (how had he known?), the flowers, the split second of recognition and then whisking me off to coffee, to hear of his success. A fleeting coffee, where he babbled (remember the brook of young lovers) his good news at me, more 'Clever Gerald's with which I concurred, where he kissed me on parting, murmured those ridiculous inconsequential nothings lovers murmur in my ear, sent me on my way, full of flowers, full of expensive and very hot coffee, topped with bubble and froth he had dabbed from my top lip (one of my arms was full of the flowers, the other had the cup – lovers do these things for each other, don't they?).

Didn't I tap dance down the street after we parted, my

heart aflame for him, as I clutched that bouquet – was that really me? Yes, of course, I did such things then, my smile as wide as wide can be, my whole body fluttering with pleasure at the very thought of him, his parting wave still imprinted on my mind's eye, his purring "See you very, very soon, my Sweet," still ringing in my ears, him winking at me as we grinned at each other. God knows how I did any work then at all.

I remember now, the office I went to for the meeting after I had left him rather well out of the flowers. They scented the whole reception, taking the hard edge off the business day. I could hardly ask for them back or indeed carry them back underground on my way home. Was this a degree of commonsense sinking in? No, no, just a practicality of the day. I would need tougher lessons in experience than this. And still, I did not think of the Ascot Girl, taken up, used, lain down, forgotten, passed over. Not then, not a second thought after that incident, did I give her. I had won the day. Which was what mattered.

It was a great pity, like all of them, it was only a twenty-four-hour day. And life goes on. It is a strange and childish belief, but I have always believed that one should die when one is happiest, as if in some way, you have reached the pinnacle of your life and that is the best time to leave it. Would this have been that day, then I should have been happy to go. When you hanker for something – or in this case, somebody – to reach it or them, to achieve what might be called possession, isn't that the zenith and after that all else is downhill? Those few minutes of such intense pleasure, of being the centre of Gerald's world, it mattered so much to me, I was dancing on the very heavens. It was such a simple thing to desire, to have Gerald's time and full attention, yet it was always just beyond achievement; I can see now I was always slotted in. By appointment.

My wish for death after such happiness was not to be. We live on and suffer much. It is the stuff of life. Bitterly now, I can look back, see the person I was then, the stubborn, passionately in love fool that I was, who would not be told, would not learn, even with all the lessons around me. Love, like water, finds its own course. Neither can be marshalled, without much difficulty and unexpected effects. And neither listen to reason. I just could not, would not, be helped. More is the pity.

7

Mrs Wendon-Davis

I have mentioned Mrs W-D. I think it is not often a man's paramour meets his wife. We English are not all as civilised as that French President's wife, Madame Mitterrand, who invited her husband's long-time lover and daughter to his funeral. I did not meet Mrs W-D as such, not till, well, the very end of what happened, but several times before then I ran into her, or found myself near her. And I went to the funeral, though not at her invitation. But there, I get ahead of myself again. I am too impatient with bitterness.

The first time we came close to each other, I remember I was in Covent Garden, seeking to replace the perfume Gerald had bought me just the previous December. It had not been a Christmas present, just something he had sent over, after a particularly long and pleasurable afternoon in bed together. He had just closed a deal on something and we celebrated, in his time-honoured fashion, "between the sheets, Sweeting! Just the thing!"

Called Elizabethan Bouquet, the perfume came from Penhaligon's, located in Wellington Street, on the edge of

Covent Garden, just up the hill from Waterloo Bridge. I remember it was in the early spring – perhaps late February, early March 1987 – and one of those lovely fresh days, where even in London, and especially near the river, the birds are all trilling to each other above the traffic noise and the air has been renewed, so that your lungs long and ache to be filled and refilled with the spring air; you can almost eat it. It is so energising it lifts you, so you feel as though you are walking on air. The sky was deepest blue (*Robin eggshell blue, à la* Gerald. *It promises more than it delivers, Sweet*). Looking back, Gerald was a great one for country sayings, considering his predominantly metropolitan lifestyle. At the time I just accepted that was Gerald. This particular spring day in London, the wind off the river was chilled, though the sun was brilliant. Still, it was a glorious day, the brightness not borne out in heat but carrying the first promise of warmth for later in the year.

So with a bounce in my step, I walked up the hill, past what used to be the Lyceum in the Strand, scene of all those Capital Radio discos back in the seventies that I had smuggled myself in, lying about my age, as all teenagers do, anxious to age themselves for a brief span of their lives, to fit in as adults. Rounding the corner from the Strand I mused perhaps I might still find my initials, carved into a brick, over several weeks, where each Friday night we had queued for what seemed hours before being let in. Only about ten years before but what a mad, carefree age that time had been, of the disco in the late seventies, I mused, as I strolled along, enjoying the day. And all that extravagant clothing, the season of glam rock. How exotic we had all been, how we had all danced, hour after hour, night after night, to all those songs now only played as classic hits on Radio 2 or marketed as collectors' CDs in Marks & Spencer. What a long time ago it all seemed. How we had staked everything on faking our ages, dressing far beyond our years, spending hours over the costume and the make-up. And hours in the toilets, turning this way and that, to ensure the view was just right. See how the spring air had affected me, setting my mind free to wander after all the winter constraints of weather and clothing.

Without any trouble, I found the shop, which had a window Americans love to call Dickensian, but the English, (*in our superior way* as per Gerald), probably know better as listed. The window, full of lopsided panes of glass, was old-fashioned and full of beautiful bottles and creams and brushes and leather goods. It is a good shop to go to when you need to treat yourself. I was looking forward to it. Perhaps I might buy other things in the same range, a bath oil perhaps, some soap. There was a wonderful heady smell of perfume as I pushed open the door with a happy sigh, the prospect of some lovely purchases ahead of me. In front, and stretching away from me, was a very beautiful rug covering the old wooden floor. All over the shop, amid the leather goods, unguents, perfumes and soaps, were tiny vases of snowdrops, plucked from beautiful, chilled obscurity in quiet woodlands somewhere in England, bringing their harbinger of the renewal of life, into a London shop. It was a very restful setting, the scent and the tiny spring flowers, cool even under the intense shop lights.

Without hurrying, I found the perfume right near the back of the shop, in between the bottles for Lily of the Valley and the Violet collection. There were bowls of snowdrops everywhere. It was terribly elegant, a very restful and calm atmosphere. Enjoying that and not really thinking terribly hard, I put my hand out and in the same second another hand shot out – a well-manicured, long-fingered hand – narrowly missing a nearby vase and causing the contained snowdrops to nod vigorously. The faster moving hand, owner yet unseen, clasped the box of perfume. The very last box. I looked up then to see who the other person was. Our eyes met as her fingers closed possessively around it.

I still remember recoiling in recognition. It was Mrs Wendon-Davis. As close as I have ever been to her. I might have gasped, almost as though she had slapped my face. Of course, she hadn't, but in a distant part of my mind, schooled by Gerald, I could see the headline, *MP accosts husband's mistress in perfume row*, or something similar. Not good – I could imagine Gerald tutting, as he paced the floor with that night's paper in hand, folded back to the gossip column, perhaps with a picture topping the article, as I nursed a black eye. 'Couldn't you have ducked, Sweeting...?' But that was nonsense, my imagination was running wild.

Coming back to reality, realigning myself to the shock, as my eyes widened, hers narrowed slightly, her lips tightened, she was determined, like a cat about to hiss, preparing to ward off invaders. She must have assumed I knew her from the television, but she was clearly not relinquishing her intended purchase by any magnanimous gesture. After all, the budding cynic in me suggested, I was not a constituent – they were all safely stowed away in north-east Norfolk, shades of that sceptical comment from a politician to a teenager, in Eddie Cochran's *Summertime Blues*, along the lines of: "I'd help you but you're not part of my electorate." How very apt.

There was no sign of recognition on her part, nor should there have been. She probably thought I was related to a fish, as my mouth silently opened and closed several times in shock, struggling in an alien environment to find the right chemicals to keep my body functioning. In the same second, as we were looking at each other – the perfume still in her clenched hand – the shop assistant hurried over at a gallop. "Madam, madam, we have more, gift wrapped. May I find you another?" And as I stepped back, battered with the shock of seeing Gerald's wife and so close, Mrs W-D – not knowing who I was – lifted the box, pursed her red lips together, turned on her heel and stalked down the shop, her shoes clicking on the wooden floor, to pay for her purchase. "Possession," as Gerald would often tell me, as he took me to bed in happier times "is nine tenths of the law." I wonder now why I recalled his words then.

I watched her go. I was crushed. My happy spirits had been whisked away from me, as a jealous, possessive child rips a toy from his most innocent friend, who was only intending to play with it. As with Gerald, so she had got there before me – but this time I could hardly borrow her perfume as I did her husband. The shop assistant hurried back, looking at me in a worried fashion, bringing more perfume, gift wrapped. Just as Gerald came to me, not as a husband but clean, fresh and gift-wrapped. Obviously not virginally gift wrapped but very chic just the same. My intentions of exploring the rest of the range were as abruptly curtailed as my mood; I bought only the perfume and left.

Thinking further on it… imagine it, his wife and I shared the same perfume, his wife and his mistress. In the dark, just awoken, how would he know us apart? How weird was that, that we smelt the same way? Was there nothing that Gerald brought to our relationship that was new and specific and unique to me, mine alone? Was it all recycled? But in many ways, Gerald was like royalty. "Never explain, never complain." It was apparent that day that he bought the perfume because that was what he liked to smell, never mind that he obviously bought it for more than one woman in his life. What perfume, for example, had he bought his mother? But I never asked, indeed I don't think I ever mentioned this incident to him. And neither did Mrs W-D, since – as far as I am aware, she had no reason to of course – she had no idea what I looked like. It is remarkable, with the wisdom of years suffered since this incident, that I was so naïve, so shocked by it, that I never asked Gerald anything about it. What a strange thing, to smell the same as your lover's wife.

One day, long afterwards but it did stay with me for months, I mentioned this uncomfortable and, to me, rather shocking incident to a friend, who smiled rather sadly, incredulous at my gullibility. "When he leaves you, he goes back to her, and he smells of her perfume. It is one less thing to worry about," she remarked. She went on, chuckling of her own affair with a married man, "I bought the perfume his wife uses and I spray his shirt with it before he leaves me. Mind you, I don't wear it myself, can't stand the stuff!" Occasionally now I smell that perfume on someone else and I am reminded of my ignorance. What a fool I was in those days. I do not wear the perfume any longer.

Then, one summer in the late eighties – and quite by chance, though it seems wholly unbelievable now – it so happened that I took a brief holiday in north-east Norfolk. It was completely un-Gerald related and I had been to that coastline as a child. It was on a whim one awful Monday in June after a rainy Sunday, that fed up with London, I thought it would be nice to have a long weekend in the country and where better, than a weekend in the country beside the sea?

So I rang a hotel that looks over the north Norfolk marshes at Blakeney, and the idea of getting away kept me going that whole week – during which, for some reason, I hardly saw Gerald. That was unusual, not to see him at least two or three times a week, most weeks, whether for his 'aperitif' speech or a lunch, or drinks in the cocktail hour. Remarkably for once, I did not check what he intended to do that weekend, and for some reason (perhaps we had had what passed for a row), I did not think clearly, did not put the two areas together consciously, or even three, the location of my hotel, a long glass-fronted flint building overlooking the old harbour, the constituency of Mrs W-D (which was one of the last things I would have thought about then) and High Fold. After all, the letterheads Gerald wrote to me under did not specify a village or town.

It was a pleasant weekend in high summer, the air light and warm even on the coast, and I relaxed. It was perfect, just what I needed. I was well looked-after and I slept the sleep of babes, to the accompaniment of the 'ting, ting, ting' of rope against yacht masts below my window, after a day walking over the marshes in the sun and wind, along the channels left by the retreating tide, and completed by an excellent meal and most of a bottle of wine. I remember the wine waiter looking askance at the remains of the bottle – 'less for them in the kitchen', as Gerald would have muttered as we sallied forth from the table, arm in arm, leaving something of a wreck behind us. Even if he wasn't there, it was as if he was. Gerald at table, with the wine list and a good menu, was like a child with a playbox.

Next day, there was a church fete at the top end of the village away from the sea. When I was a child, we used to go to these frequently, my mother being a keen supporter of the WI and hence the church. Taking a sun hat, as the sun even that early was fierce, I climbed up the hill from the quayside, up the narrow lane, lined on both sides by what was once fishermen's cottages but had become the enclave of the weekender, seeking more frequent refuge than I from London. You can tell the weekender cottage: the security alarm is imported as a concept from a London borough close to the top of the crime scale, while the blinds are pulled down when the place is unoccupied, in some vain delusion that whilst it stops you looking in, this will not advertise that the place is empty.

Apropos of Gerald and his comments on the church in Blythburgh, now years before, en route up the hill (who said Norfolk is flat?) I noted through the trees, the church's second smaller tower, halfway along the ridge of the nave. The waiter in the hotel informed me – as he leaned over the wine bottle I was to empty utterly that evening – that the second tower was a beacon sailors once lined up to, to come into the now silting-up harbour.

The fete was very well attended. There were many of the WI-types, all smiles and lovely rounded bosomy ladies, blue-rinsed even this far north. Clearly many people knew each other. Lots of hellos, carolling across the field mixed with a bit of 'Darling, how nice'; many children running about, mixed in with early holidaymakers, keen to get a break before the invasion of families, freed from the tyranny of the school run. Lots of well-dressed, white-haired, very smart men, ties, quite a lot of straw hats, military types, retired, strolling about after their wives. It was a very English scene, green, full of sunshine, the church in the background, cottages, the sea air, the stalls and people just stepping out in the country. There were a variety of small tables and stalls long familiar from childhood; the raffle, a tombola run by two very sturdy ladies, the guess the number of sweets in the bottle, the weight of the cake, then a very upmarket bring-and-buy stall, a plant stall and one for homegrown vegetables, which was mobbed by people buying from it to take back to London. Imagine that, the freshest of vegetables served on a Monday night to the foodie intelligentsia – could they spot the difference between country grown and supermarket purchased? This was long before the farmers' market movement of the late nineties got under way, but the desire was the same.

I looked up from an array of jams, pickles and chutneys. This had been my mother's particular forte, turning out bottles and jars of that season's product, each topped with one of those funny round greaseproof paper things. My job had always been to put the elastic band over the completed item and put the label on. And of course, to lick out the bowl. These in front of me now were much more upmarket than I recalled from my childhood kitchen, these were computer-generated labels, named the branch of the WI, what the product was and who had made it. How things move on when you are least expecting it. However, from this gastronomic comparison, of my mother's efforts thirty or more years before and those before me now, I looked up, and there was Gerald.

It was a shock. It was not that I had forgotten him, it was just that I least expected to see him. My heart turned over, my stomach contracted at the very sight of him, like an electric spark along a wire. He had not seen me, he was standing with a small boy in front of a stall with one of those electric wire contractions, along which the small boy was trying to carry a wire ring, without touching the electrified wire. If he touched it, which I realised now that others had before him, the electrified wire would ring out a loud 'bleep' and the wire ring had to be taken back to the start and the game begun afresh. Gerald was watching the boy's hand intently, standing alongside him, well bent forward in concentration, both hardly daring to breathe. The boy's hand crept along the wire. Up it went, following an upturn, over the top of the curve, halfway along the whole system, when 'bleep'. Gerald and the unknown child collapsed their lungs. The wire ring came back to the start and the process began again.

After the third time, the game was over. The boy, running, ran from the stall and Gerald, elegant, elegant Gerald even here, relaxed and off-duty, ambled after him. "Couldn't do it," he called to someone. "We tried, didn't we Greg? But it was not to be." And he ruffled the hair of the small boy, whom he had caught up with. And there was Mrs Wendon-Davis. Well, it was her, but different. My breath drew in. I only knew her really from the television. And those few fleeting seconds in Penhaligon's... and here was a clone. Could there be two Mrs W-Ds? Could she really clone? No, no, the second must be her sister – the likeness was quite extraordinary. And the small boy belonged to the sister, as he was now holding her hand and using her arm as a lever to jump up and down, whilst the trio of adults listened to his replay of the game.

Gerald and Mrs W-D. Together in front of me. Well, the jams and pickles were forgotten. I must have gasped. Unconsciously my hand was rising to my mouth. I found it there and dropped it, recovering myself. A lady even came along the stall then to ask if I needed help. Seeing me look, she turned to see what had caught my eye. "Oh, yes," she said realising what I was looking at, "that's our local MP and her husband. We may be a bit off the beaten track, but we do have a quite special MP. She's very good, comes every year. She'll be along in a minute to buy something, does every summer. Been coming since she was a girl. She's very good to us."

At this, I came to my senses, smiled, as she was saying, "And he's a nice man, her husband, a very pleasant man, works in London, but he's here most weekends…" I nodded some inanity, and backed away, jam-less, other things on my mind. I could have left, perhaps I should. But I didn't. Believe it or not, it did not occur to me.

Mrs Wendon-Davis. In the flesh. There she was in front of me. Smaller than on the television, no bright green suit, but a dress, sprigged cotton, green of course. And on duty, amongst her constituents. She did not see me, did not register me, did not recognise me from the incident in the perfumery, months, or perhaps a year or so, before. But of course, I knew her. Television dismisses, even negates, your privacy when you are in the public eye, as do the papers. I think that week she had been in the headlines, for some comment she had made about Europe. I had not followed it; I was not interested in her thoughts, only those of her husband. That day the hair was redder than when last I had seen her on television, clamped as ever to her head, like a swimming cap. Nothing to ruffle or tumble down, nothing wanton. Bottle-red. Over the years it has varied from blonde with red, to red with blonde, to red. Her dress was firmly buttoned and belted. No chance of anything escaping there, nothing to tumble forth. No 'ooo' factor as Gerald would say, as in his oft-repeated "ooo, is that all for me?" at sight of feminine curves in pretty underwear, his fingers crinkling in anticipation, rather as a chocoholic might do at the sight of a freshly opened box of truffles or something similar, salivating at what delights might lie ahead. And Gerald did not touch her, no friendly hug or embrace. He knew his place. This was her domain. In the public eye. All present and correct. No wonder she used so much hairspray. Another person might wonder what had brought them together, attracted one to the other. But it was not my question, not one I cared to consider or to dwell on. As I watched them, he and she stood over the child, who was making them laugh still.

Shaking slightly, rather chilled with shock, I had a cup of tea in the marquee. And one of those nice homemade scones with lots of jam (Women's Institute jam – how discerning my mother would have been in trying it) and cream. Think of how different it is, to watch someone, with whom normally you lock eyes with and those eyes remain conscious of each other whatever else happens. You are drawn back and back to each other, almost visually manacled to each other, despite the reason why you are really there. But this time Gerald had not seen me. His eyes were still free. Thus I watched Gerald free of that connection, Gerald the married man, Gerald the faithful chap, Gerald the MP's husband, moving amongst his friends and neighbours, shaking hands, patting backs, laughing at a shared joke, Greg his shadow, sometimes slipping his small paw into Gerald's so-manicured, so-soft hand. Did it break my heart to see them together, so terribly innocent, so terribly fond of each other? I was not envious, only caught on an unforeseen razor edge of emotion, that this was something I could not give him or share.

About three, a cry went up: "Phototime, photos, everyone over here please." We assembled, or were assembled, under a huge oak tree, with the church in the background. People were directed, according to height, so that everyone was included appropriately and everyone's face could be seen, as a record of the day. As it happens, I have a copy of that photo. Gerald and Mrs W-D are centre stage. Gerald has Greg in front of him, and Gerald's hand is on Greg's shoulder. The love between them, the man and the child, is very apparent, even what is it, fifteen, twenty years later? Greg was probably about eight then. I wonder what he thinks of Gerald now. Clearly then it was hero worship. The photo should be part of that golden sun-filled childhood hopefully the memory of which Greg carries with him still.

I am not in that picture. Astonishingly, too late it came to me that I should not have been there, should not have stayed. Hurrying, I moved away, and it was then that Gerald saw me, even with the hat. Perhaps there is something in the way I walk, or as Gerald would have drawled "Something, Sweeting about the way you stroll" and put it into a hum. He liked to think he was musical.

After the photo was taken, he came after me, found me having another cup of tea. It was a very public arena, very quiet in the marquee, some of the ladies retrieving tea towels after the picture gathering, resuming their washing-up. "Sweeting!" he whispered and loudly, in his big hail-fellow-well-met voice, said, "Hello and how nice to see you," as if I was one of his wife's constituents. We shook hands, playing the game. It was terribly formal. "What are you doing here?" he mouthed and out loud, "Yes, how very nice," which was very Gerald-like. "And you are?" as he winked at me. In a second, I went from wanting to cry, from being an outsider, to the delight of his smile, hidden from the tea ladies, the familiar and much-loved grey eyes twinkling into mine, and yes, I could see, after the shock, it was a pleasure. He knew I would be discreet and so I was. Think now what power I had, and never knew of. Only the very next month, July 1988, the boss of Burton, the clothing company whose phrase "Gone for a Burton" has become part of the language, was in the spotlight and all over the tabloids, in a court case over the alleged theft of diaries in which his lady friend very specifically detailed her affair with him, a knight of the realm. Just think what I could have done, the work of seconds, wrecking so much. But then, at the time, it did not occur to me. Later, only much later...

I have some other photos of that day, presumably from a press release Mrs W-D's office liked to put out. Mine came with an advertising campaign the hotel was putting on, for holidays later in the summer. The photo in question is in the middle of the brochure and is used to show the fete as a typical English summer's afternoon event in the village. There is Mrs W-D well to the fore, and Gerald and Greg slightly behind her, to one side. No one is holding hands. Greg is squinting into the sun, looking up at Gerald. And behind them all, still further, right near the back of the picture, is a person in a sun hat, just outside their circle, standing watching them. And that person is me.

Chilling is it not, to have a photo of a man and his wife, and the man's lover?

8

The Lot of the Mistress

It is the lot of the mistress, poor fool that she is, to be alone at Christmas. And family holidays, the interminable summer holiday, one at Easter perhaps, the odd long weekend. Of course, the same is true over the other milestones in family history. When you are waiting upon the attentions of a man whose attentions are legally elsewhere, you do not – cannot – commit to your own life. My own family began quite early on to give up inviting me to their social events. One of my sisters-in-law was heard to sneer of me: "Don't bother to ask, you know she'll be waiting for her fancy man. You know she'll say no, she's busy. We all know what she's doing. Though why she waits in for him I can't imagine," before her opinion was stifled – one of my brothers seeing me coming, hushing her up, with the look that passes between couples that does not need words. But not before I had heard her. After a while, those invitations normally extended to maiden sisters, aunts, godmothers, dried up. And I could not blame them, my brothers and their wives. My mother suffered for me though. And my dad? Well, he would not talk of it, that I was the mistress of a married man.

The life of a mistress is always by proxy. The Wendon-Davis family occasions, the weddings, the christenings (Gerald had no children – was this more tailoring?), the funerals, are always at one remove and any contact with such occasions is either before ("Is my tie straight?") or afterwards ("Look at the ridiculous smile on her, like the cat who has had the cream. The money more like.") via photographs, and – in Gerald's case – often the press, to milk the connection if such were needed. I knew his whole family, their names, connections, successes, histories; Gerald bought masses of photos after each wedding or any other event and identified them for me, so that I knew them intimately by picture be it colour or monochrome, watched them change and develop but none of them face to face in the living person. And of course, none of them for years and years knew anything about me. Other than a possible existence, and that probably only a suspicion of Mrs W-D, if she cared to reflect occasionally.

At Christmas though, the loneliest time of the year, all those maudlin songs have it about right. What clever lyricists. I have often wondered how many Christmases they have spent alone, to achieve such knowledge. How I adored him, how life itself seemed empty and ridiculous without him. Now, looking back, how ridiculous it all was, I was. My sister-in-law, with her hardly veiled scorn, was right. It was largely in the days before mobile phones, a time the young cannot credit and, looking back now, I can't think why I did stay in for him, waited by the phone, willed it to ring. But then, then at that emotive time of year, it all seemed the right thing to do, to wait for him, for his call. Waiting at that time of year takes on a different meaning. Do not dwell on this over long, but think of that combination of childhood memories, that seeking of the familiar, the carols that make you cry for times and people past. And for those whom you are not with, willingly or not, guilt-ridden notwithstanding. For my part, I cannot sing 'Silent Night' without the tears coursing soundlessly down my cheeks. In my mind's eye, I am back in the church of my childhood, my brothers, my parents around me. I can see the greenery for the altar vases, tall sticks of bay and rosemary, dark green against the brown wood and the gold of the cross and the vases, no flowers in Advent on the altar. It is always Christmas Eve communion. Back in the present, as I cried, sometimes Gerald would be there to mop the tears' progress and pull me to him, wordlessly – take me into the curve of his arm. If I am honest, more often he was not there. Now of course… but I get ahead of myself again.

As a mistress, it is impossible to be with other people at such a time, all those memories of happier Christmases, all those successful lovers, all those relatives for whom time means other than the bated breath, the listening, the waiting for the lover to call. By your very status you are isolated, caught in an intake of time, waiting for life to resume, after New Year, into January and the return to work, normal life. But whilst you wait, bated breath, the guilt does not escape you, the desire to return to places and people familiar; all is on hold – jammed up in you – waiting for the loved one, the desired one to contact you.

Gerald seemed to sense this. Some years the weekend before Christmas he would appear on the doorstep clutching a small tree in a pot in one hand and goodies in the other. Looking back now, it all seems so clichéd, so Hollywood-like, such a fantasy. We would spend the afternoon with squeals of delight, decorating and redecorating its branches. It was, of course, ludicrous that it took so long but we had mince pies and sherry or port amid much kissing and laughter, singing along to carols on the radio. Gerald knew a lot of wicked alternatives to the standard verses. If he could not remember the words, he made up ribald and always droll choruses. Sometimes, of course, we coupled, as Gerald would put it and, then naked, decorate each other and the tree afresh, amid fresh giggles. On such occasions the carolling became quite saucy.

Other years I decorated the tree without him. A Christmas tree however small should not be dressed alone. The mince pies and sherry do not taste the same. The afternoon would dawdle and I had dressed the tree before I knew it. I would marvel then, in the quiet of the flat, that with Gerald we could make it last all afternoon and have trouble finishing it before he left, driving off into the winter darkness, to begin the journey to High Fold.

If then I could not have Gerald, I was in his thoughts. A hamper would arrive, usually sometime on Christmas Eve. I hate to say this, but even in the height of new love I did wonder that first Christmas had there been someone before me, that Gerald knew the form? Probably. It might be naïve to think otherwise. Perhaps, I comforted myself, it had been years before. The kindest thing I could say is that Wendy, Gerald's secretary – the inestimable Wendy – arranged it. Later, I would know for certain. It is as well not to dwell on the historical reasons for such things.

But imagine, from the hamper, which was such a kindness on his part (or the parcel to assuage his guilt?), the indescribable poignancy of opening a bottle of champagne alone. That 'pop' into silence. Just me. Just me on my own. Champagne deserves a crowd. A collective 'ooh' as it is opened. A 'hurray' even, several hurrays and cheering, some clapping. Not quiet, the quiet of being alone. I drank it of course. And drinking it, suffered the acidity settling on my stomach, long after the Queen's words on faith, hope, duty and long service. I would come, after that first Christmas, to know all about long service. And hope.

As the dusk came down, and the lights came on with the chill, I would walk through London, through the deserted streets, the deserted parks, to the lights on Regent Street, as fake as my season of goodwill. To the shop windows crammed with goods, counting down to the start of the sales. I would walk and walk, against the wind, chilled, frozen, filled with the bitterness of solitary champagne. If Gerald had been there, oh if and if and if… he would have called it *a lazy wind, Sweeting, it goes through you, not round you.* But he wasn't of course, and I just walked, occupying time, head down, into the wind. Eventually, utterly chilled, numb with cold, nipped fingers, frozen stumps for toes, appalled with the silence of solitude and the empty streets, I would turn back to the warmth and glow of my flat for some of the fruitcake from the hamper. Real comfort eating, late afternoon, the curtains closed against the dark, a glass of milk to counter the acid and masses of cake. Lots of cherries – Wendy chose cake well.

Sometimes, if I was lucky, there would be one of Gerald's worn shirts in the washing bin. After one particularly awful and lonely Christmas, I made sure the next year and all those that followed, that Gerald left a shirt, by hiding it as he left one morning, saying I would wash it for next time.

Gerald was the sort of man who kept spare shirts all over the place. Then in the evening of Christmas Day – when in other homes, tea is being prepared, the children have worn down the batteries of their toys, the hundredth cup of tea is being drunk – I could snuggle up with the shirt and eat cake crumbles all over it, basking in the faint scent of lavender it still exuded. Think not of his words "Let her eat cake," whilst he partied away, or whatever he did at High Fold during that season. Think only of its warming comfort and the familiarity of that scented crumpled cotton.

In the early days, those very early Christmases in our relationship, repeats of *Morecambe and Wise* would make me laugh, drying my tears, and then I would join a sort of community all across the country. Or a Bond film, endless repeats of James Bond, glamorous, derring-do, timelessly handsome, timelessly elegant, always proficient, saving the world from some baddie. Time, retirement, death and Mr Murdoch eventually put paid to that common coming together, that last visage of communal viewing. But before then, sometimes, some Christmases – well indeed, I should say most – Gerald would ring, from High Fold. I was not forgotten, he was just required elsewhere. On duty. Such is the plight of those who fall in love with people already taken elsewhere. It is not an excuse, but it is true that everyone has a choice, it is just that some of us missed the turning or were asleep at the crossroads when the decision was made. Or halfway down an abyss. And still falling.

You can imagine then the utter pleasure, the unmitigated delight in being asked to accompany Gerald on a trip. Not accompany him in the same way that Mrs W-D, in normal circumstances, as the wife of a businessman would, but go to the place he was going to, be with him when he was not on duty, share his bed, perhaps even share breakfast. Don't think of that politician in the eighties, a woman too, who suggested men take their wives with them, to act as a kind of condom, when AIDS was at its publicity-driven, terrified height. When you are fool enough to sit at the table of love, where by rights – legal, marital rights – the place is already filled, such crumbs mean a paradise, and your normal daily companions, Loneliness, Doubt and Pain, are temporarily held at bay. Deception – self-deception – and Delusion – delusion of the self – take over, heavily disguised of course. See how full of aphorisms I am now. How so very wise, afterwards. Now I see I was taken along, as… well at best as 'arm candy' (a Gerald-ism for a pretty girl), if nothing else.

We went to Italy several times, a few times to Germany. He would fly out business class and I would follow, on a later flight, tickets provided by Gerald (paid for by Mrs W-D's lovelies?), delivered care of Wendy, who arranged everything. In Italy, we stayed in Milan at the Four Seasons, and breakfasted overlooking the formal gardens before he went off to make Connections and I wandered happily enough through the shopping quarter. We stayed in Sardinia, in Sicily, in hotels where the sound of the sea lulled us to sleep and the cries of the fishermen marked our first waking. Does this sound like the stuff of Mills & Boon? Of course it does. Who cares. Happy? I was delirious. These were some of our happiest hours together.

For one of my birthdays, we flew our separate ways as usual to Rome. As ever, the ticket arrived in good time, there was a car to the airport and a hotel car to pick me up from the airport, which is some distance from Rome. Gerald, in the guise of Wendy, was generosity and kindness itself. Nothing was too much trouble. Who cares how I was described, as a write-off against tax or the declaration on the expenses?

On every flight, there is always a person who makes the most noise, causes the most problems, talks loudly and presumes to take up most of the space. The one on this flight was a large, balding man, just across the aisle but one seat forward, who clearly thought two seats was his due. He tutted before take-off when a fellow passenger came rightly to claim the seat next to him, forcing the fat man to move the pile of books and papers he had put possessively on the seat. The air hostess made him relinquish them to her during the take-off preparations, which he did so most reluctantly, pestering her almost immediately after take-off and the belts sign had gone off to have them back again. For what seemed like almost the whole flight, he kept ringing the bell for the stewardess and when drinks came round he asked for more to be brought, unopened, "Something for later," as though free drinks were a right and, when she brought the bottles, he pushed them deep into his bag. I was disturbed sufficiently from my book to look up and see him wink at the stewardess – what they have to put up with – as though that somehow excused his greed. As we flew over the Alps, we had to ascend, to avoid turbulence; as a result, the cabin crew were delayed serving coffee, to protect everyone from spillages. The large man voiced his opinion of that, very loudly. He kept mopping his brow, clearly, he was very uncomfortable. But what was strangest of all, whenever I looked up, I could see him several times looking at me, as if I were an unusual specimen. Collected already, elsewhere, by someone else, I wanted to shout.

Once landed at Rome, he demanded to be allowed off the plane first, as though he were a VIP or disabled, when in reality I think he just wanted to continue the fuss he had created during the flight. I was relieved when he went, though even before he went through the aircraft door and down the steps, he looked back, straight at me. I was chilled at his expression, invaded by it. One last look at the uncollectible?

Rome that night truly was *la dolce vita*. Our hotel was close to the top of the Spanish Steps. When I arrived, there was the usual bottle of bubbly on ice, the white napkin draped over the top. Gerald sang in the bath, very deep, pretending to be American. "Strangers in the tub…" Everything was a-sparkle, everywhere was a-glow. "Sharing bubbles". That is how is it is when you are in love. From the echoing bathroom, more Gerald: "What were the chances we'd be sharing soap before the bath was throughooooo?" He soaked the bathroom, wrecked the towels. Nanny's influence did not extend this far. Did we care? Of course not. It was our evening. We were going to be in love for ever. Weren't we? "Do be do be do," sang Gerald, shaving.

We went out to dinner. It was a February night, but even then the steps were lit, golden glowing under the night sky. Is it not the most beautiful city in the world when there are two of you and you are in love? Coming from London, still under inches of chill and frost, it was a warm early spring evening, though the Italian women went on wearing their furs. There, image is all. A true triumph of style over necessity. "Do you think, Sweet," queried Gerald, his head turning seemingly through 360 degrees to admire a beauty in furs passing us, "they wear anything underneath?"

So we strolled down the Steps, amid, even in February, bowls of flowers on the intermittent terraces. We could hold hands. We were free as we never truly were on London's streets. It truly was the city for lovers. That evening, he was all mine. I could hear the music, the 'Moonlight Sonata', Beethoven's wooing of the moon, the piano's notes dropping into the hum of the distant traffic. Did we dance by the light of the moon, the moon, or was it just the lamplights? Who cares? We were a long way downriver from that babbling brook, but things were still good, still flowing.

There is a secret restaurant tucked under the Steps, at the bottom. It is not secret to Romans of course, but hidden from outsiders. Gerald, with the connections, was of course in the know. The call had been made, the reservation agreed. There was no need for him to propel or to impress me. We were just able to be lovers, out to dinner. So let the evening commence, the orchestra in full flow, unchecked.

When two people dine, who are interested in, nay, fascinated by each other, who are friends, who are lovers, whatever, the rest of the room can go quietly to hell. And so it was. We talked and talked and smiled and laughed. Our fingers fluttered, our eyes danced. Liberated in Rome, away from the constraints in London, was there something else in our body language that trumpeted our relationship across the room? Who knows? But halfway through dessert the light over the table changed. Gerald and I looked round. I was aware that his face froze.

"Gerald," said the man casting the very large shadow, blocking out the other diners. "How nice. May I sit down?" And without waiting, he did so. "And who is this lovely? The mouse's latest playmate? And how is Mrs Wendon-Davis? I believe the House is still sitting, even at this late hour." All apparently in one breath; I have put in the full stops for him. Killing the conversation, the atmosphere. The pianist in my head stopped playing, almost mid note, and shut the piano. It was the man from the plane, still sweating (even Gerald would not have corrected me here. The man was sweating). Who was this man?

For a long minute, which really was seconds, I thought it was the onset of the ice age on Gerald's face. The reflection on his glasses hid the expression in his eyes from the unknown man, but I could see the muscles round his eyes from the side, saw the wince, as his eyes narrowed, assessing his opponent, the split second his lips pursed. Then as the ice age receded, as his face melted, he recovered himself, his lips smoothed, shock became the pleasure of Gerald's act; this one headed "How to react when meeting another Englishman abroad one does not like". "David," he said, with genuine insincerity, "how interesting!" Not the conventional 'how nice', or 'what a pleasure'.

I was introduced. Gerald was almost flirting with the man. Flirting with a blade, not his eyelashes. I was "a colleague". I could all but see the man writing my name down. Certainly he made a mental note, one eyebrow arched, all his chins mobile, even as he mopped his face. I wanted to melt into the curtains conveniently behind me. Could I still hear the lesson from the tailors and Mr George? No exit there. Besides, I was sitting down. It was difficult to get away.

Close to the end of the evening, the head waiter brought over complimentary sambucas. Gerald would always attract these sorts of gifts. To compound the felony of his continuing presence at our table, my erstwhile companion from the plane joined us in the round of drinks, or rather, putting it another way, at that stage he did not leave. The drinks arrived, all with the obligatory floating coffee bean, and much bowing and scraping. Gerald was clearly well respected there. The head waiter duly returned with his matches, to undertake the ceremony of lighting the alcohol, bending over each glass, coaxing the matches to perform. Each tiny glass, cherished by the head waiter, began to dance with the flame on the surface of the liquid.

It is difficult to say exactly what happened next, but it is possible – indeed I am certain – that one of Gerald's more flamboyant gestures with his arms akimbo, took with it David's (I have forgotten his surname now) glass. The flame was carried with the tide. 'Whoomph' went the flame, in one of Gerald's more impressive moments, as the liquor surged over the tablecloth, which subsequently burst into greater flame, concurrent with an audible, collective gasp from the tables around us. Like a tide, everyone about us leaned back in their chairs, to get as far from the flames as possible. Or, as Gerald later suggested, "to obtain a grandstand view. You know, Sweeting, they're Italian, they love that sort of entertainment."

As we leapt back, Gerald, with a roar (I want to say, like a lion…), leapt to his feet. His chair crashed onto the tile floor all genuine Italian restaurants are required by some Greater Law to have. There was another ripple of movement across the room. I half expected him to pick up the chair, rather as though he were fighting a bull, not a fire. "Dear God, man," he cried as though it was the other man's fault. He tossed his mane back (yes, really) as though it were really in the way, Gerald not being one to forego a theatrical gesture where possible. Clearly having taken lessons from some of London's finest firemen, who usually arrive by fire engine rather than Tarzan's rope – but that is my imagination running away – with a great studied effort on his face, he plunged his napkin into the water jug, causing a tidal wave of water to surge from it, much of which washed over David whatever his name was, whereupon Gerald began mopping the table – to put the fire out – and mopping the David person, to prevent him and all his chins, dripping. It was a very pretty purple and green flame, licking rather delicately, for all Gerald's efforts, around the tablecloth. A second surge of water from Gerald, who had picked up a jug from an adjoining table, washed over the table, again much of it ending in David's lap, who jumped in his seat and spluttered at another onslaught. People began to rise around us. Some began to clap. The *maître d'* hurried over, more napkins to the fore, but by then Gerald's efforts had succeeded in putting out the mini-inferno. The tablecloth was a sorry ruin but Gerald stood, looking noble, shoulders back, his chest full of pride, like the matador who has killed the bull, to take the applause, which the whole restaurant joined in on. No, no, thinking about it again, Gerald taking the ovation as his due, stood like the Emperor at the Games, the charred remains of the cloth before him, waving his rather burned napkin in recognition. Unlike the Emperor though, in view of what happened afterwards, Gerald did not turn down his thumb. The audience deemed the inferno cabaret and cheered and clapped appropriately. Clearly it was an occupational hazard as far as the *maître d'* was concerned.

As the applause began to fall away and Gerald sat down, he murmured, "David, I am most terribly sorry," in his greatest Oscar-winning voice. Even I recognised that it contained not even the whiff of the tiniest murmur of what I would recognise as sincerity. David-person bowed his head and accepted what was only a verbal apology, with nothing I could sense behind it of decency or validity. Perhaps he was used to such things. Certainly his suit seemed to wear it all well, but then perhaps it had seen other such events, on other such evenings.

Even then, in spite of the obvious dampness and thus presumable discomfort of his suit, the David-person took an indecent time to leave. When he finally went, Gerald apparently unruffled and adjusting his cuffs to a still-pristine white shirt, said, in his best dark-brown voice: "As you may have noticed, Sweeting, I am allergic to that man."

He caught the waiter's eye, who as ever scuttled over, if an Italian can ever be seen to do such an inelegant thing. Gerald ordered more drinks, as if it was the most normal evening. The waiter, bowing, clearly impressed with the evening's cabaret performance, smiled and turned away to bring them, knowing there would be a large tip. Turning back to me, Gerald went on in an undertone, as though this were the most normal state of affairs, "He has all the manners and personality of a fart," another from the Gerald magpie collection of phrases. "I think we need to employ a little damage limitation here. For good form's sake, we may have to make one or two changes. Another room, at least for tonight. Nothing personal, just being cautious. We'll have other evenings." This was most unlike Gerald. For a start, it was a whole sentence, several of them actually. You will have noticed that Gerald rarely strung a whole sentence together but put bits of them out, with terms of affection strewn among the words. It was a sign of how serious this was, that suddenly his mind constructed the sentence and delivered it, whole. It was something I had learned he did if Mrs W-D was in serious danger of being put in the picture. Taking the wider view, I like to think that it was also protection for me. No farm gate appearances if at all possible. The man from the plane, who had taken the delight of the evening from us, turned out to be a journalist. This was long before the Bentley incident and the tattooed strawberry later draped all over the paper. Then in the Bentley, Gerald was more careful, or perhaps more calculating, and would only allow himself to be caught on his terms. I remember the tattooed strawberry went on to become one of those big names, who are famous for being famous. And Gerald made many more connections as a result. Remember (one of Gerald's mottos), there is no such thing as bad publicity, only some you have to take time to live down. "Roll with the punches, Sweet," he would say, "go with the flow," making an upper cut with his fist in the air.

But now, in Rome, that lovely February evening, full of the promise of an early spring, the sap rising, the season of love, this David-person had ruined the evening. The lovely new lingerie, bought specially for the romantic night that had been ahead, would be unsurveyed that evening. No 'well, this *is* nice', in Gerald's special dark-chocolate voice reserved for such occasions, as he would undo whatever 'it' was, as though a man selecting a particularly favoured confection from a special and expensive selection. No more 'do be do be do' that night. All those careful unguents, potions, the scent behind the knees (yes, really), the dabbing of perfume on all the heat spots, what care I took in those days, all for nought. This man had the measure of Gerald and now he thought he had something on Gerald. Me. If I was carefree, here of course I would have said *but what difference does one more make to the list you have been linked to*, but of course, I wasn't that butterfly, that carefree spirit. I was ensnared, in love, in Rome, with the man I wanted to be with. It was my birthday. The evening was ruined. Is there a more emotive combination?

And this David-person, despite Gerald's immediate and warning revenge with the sambuca, had just spoiled all that. I was the fisherman, who had had the fish of my desire within my sights, albeit only for the night; I had had my hands cupped around the fish, ready to pluck it from the water. This awful, balding, sweating man had come along and the fish had wriggled free, back to the underwater regions, the oxygen of his life. Would Gerald always be 'the one that got away'? Or got taken away?

The next day we met over breakfast. Ostentatiously, Gerald met me in the foyer, in full sight of the restaurant, smiling at others before me, as they passed, so that everyone knew we had not spent the night together, think it was a business acquaintance we were both with. I can play the part too – naïve as this action sounded. Gerald looked a bit shadowy under the eyes but otherwise he was fine. Neither of us had slept well apart.

When I asked about the man, Gerald indicated across the room and there he was, breakfasting, watching us, whilst he wore the same suit – did it have a tide mark? We both bowed and smiled, nodded, more of the 'How to react when meeting another Englishman abroad' bit and then Gerald murmured: "Those who live in the gutter generally die there."

There was little more time to think on it. I flew back to

London alone. Gerald completed his connections. This part of the story then came from Gerald. On the Saturday night at High Fold, Gerald took a call. The story for the following day's front page would be along the lines of *MP's husband in Roman tryst* or some such. There would be a photo of the two of us. In fact, though I can't now remember how or why, I have a copy of that picture. Funny really that I saw it at all. Remarkably, recalling such a painful evening, it is a very beautiful picture. It has captured that moment on the Steps, as the pianist was beginning. Gerald's face is clear, smiling at me, as the dance begins, and you can see the back of my head and my face turned up to his, like a sunflower to the sun, under the lamplight. My face, unlike she of the tattooed strawberry, is not clear, but then it is not my life the paper is out to ruin. Clearly, this particular devil had not liked Gerald's chocolates.

Wendon-Davis Associates, even late that Saturday evening, got an injunction. On what grounds, I have no idea. Remember Gerald's innumerable connections? The story did not run. But that Sunday, into Monday, the phone lines hummed. By Tuesday evening, a story was beginning to break over the wires about a journalist with the *People* and young boys in his bed. There was to be no farmyard gate rendezvous with the press. The journalist, for David whatever-his-name-was, it was, did not resign. Instead the next day's story, in some of the papers, was the discovery of his body – he had killed himself in shame, hanged himself.

It was a shattering thing. Apparently the man had had a wife and two teenage daughters. Even Gerald was shocked. He never said that he had instigated it, brought it about, made the connection. But he had. Dimly, I remembered his chilling comments about Mr Fred. This time, Gerald had known and it was a warning shot across the bows. The press and Gerald arrived at a truce, albeit an uneasy one. "Leave my private life to me." There was a line in the sand. It was the late eighties. If only the Windsors had had the same.

9

Location, Location, Location

The specific reason for Gerald buying the flat, apart from the obvious one for his convenience, has gone from my memory. It may be that Gerald had to hide some money or just get rid of it. Sometimes that happened, amazing as it may seem. Or he needed to divert some of Mrs W-D's for tax reasons. No, I think perhaps the main reason is that he just wanted to house me at a convenient location. This is the most probable to my now cynical mind.

In fact, it is not a flat; it is a shoebox, albeit a large one, at the top of a tall building near the Haymarket in London. If you are clever and stand at a certain point in the main room, a sort of sitting room (my mother, *Not a lounge, you only get lounges at airports*), you used to be able to see the river, well a very small triangle of the river, which increased and decreased with the state of the tide. In the intervening years someone has concreted over the view of the triangle.

The flat has large windows, well one large circular window and several clever inner walls and curtains divide a very small space, which if kept scrupulously tidy (shades of Nanny again here) is a reasonable living space for a small person. Gerald was not small, and at times the shoebox was full to overflowing with him. No matter, he was not there for the living space, only to visit, and to visit quickly.

Before Gerald bought it, sometime in mid-summer 1986, I was taken round, by the housekeeper of the block, not Gerald, nothing so lowly. When I saw it, it was still occupied. "Come in," hissed Molly the housekeeper, waving the same message. "Whilst the cat's away, so to speak, come and see the flat." I stepped inside the door, a bright-yellow hallway, very tiny. Bright yellow. I liked its warmth. There were coat hooks all over one wall. "Come," Molly grinned proprietarily, "but mum's the word, you haven't seen it." Nodding my promise of silence that I knew I would never be required to keep, we went into the next room, a sort of antechamber, occupied chiefly by a cat tray and several bags of litter. There were stripped pine stairs in the corner. One of the cats, a strange and tiny creature, full of secret worlds past, was relieving itself in the tray. A bloom of urine scent invaded the air. She picked it up when it had finished and we all went through the next set of double doors, the cat's purrs accompanying us, into another room, with a massive television, all black and modern and shiny, totally out of place amidst a French wire bedstead day bed, a huge gold antique mirror, a low table with gilt leaves all over the legs and a large wood burner in the fireplace. There were dried hydrangea flowers hanging from the curtain poles across the windows and thin, striped curtains pulled back to let the sun in. Behind us, in one of the quarters of the room, the ceiling had stopped short of the wall and, stepping into the gap below it, when I looked up, I could see a gallery, with a stripped pine balustrade and the bottom half of a large, curved window. The lower room was three parts of a square and in the fourth part, indeed occupying most of the space, was a French-style kitchen. With Gerald's interest in food, I could see the attraction of the place. Later, to be recalled with much pleasure, I might come home and find Gerald in a pinny – he did love cooking in a pinny – greeting me with "Try this, Sweet, just try this," and waving a wooden spoon at me or the paddle of the mixer, covered in aioli, for the first of the English season's asparagus (Gerald only ate English asparagus) or perhaps for a chocolate mousse. Gerald made chocolate mousse when things were not going well and he needed some thinking time. The kitchen might be in uproar but my fridge and often the freezer might be filled with all sorts of wonderful or exotic, sublime cooking. It was another outlet for Gerald's sensuality.

Stooping, Molly picked up some pottery. "This is all made in France, to Madam's order. I have to clean it." She sniffed and peered into a cup. "Looks like I've missed a bit there," she said, poking it with her finger. At the end of the room was a door out onto a balcony, high up above the London streets. We stood at the door and looked out. The floor was covered with bricks, basket-weave fashion, between which there were tuffs of grass and moss growing. "She's asked me to clean this up. Well, I tried, got the hoe on the weeds, those bricks… well, damp they are, oozing at this time of year. It was hopeless, trying to clean them." The view beyond the balcony wall was fabulous.

We went on round the flat. Up those pine steps, with a bend in them. We came to a landing and Molly opened the door into a bedroom. I gasped as I stepped up into it. There was a huge and very high bed, with tall carved posts on each corner, occupying at least two-thirds of the room. Clearly Madam, though a small girl-woman whom I had met once through Gerald, liked large furniture that made a statement. The bed faced towards the balustrade I had seen from downstairs and beyond that a huge circular window, looking over the west of London. High, high up in the ceiling were two skylight windows. The gallery allowed some of the light down into the room below. The whole bedroom was painted light blue and full of light, with mirrors reflecting and counter-reflecting what happened in the bed. There were no curtains anywhere. "I shouldn't like to sleep in here in high summer," I ventured. "You'd never sleep." Molly shrugged; presumably sleeping was not one of Madam's priorities. Off that room in an alcove was a small area painted with Tintin and a rocket. I dimly remembered them from comic-book days. Clearly, Madam's decorating powers had not yet got that far. Presumably the previous owner had painted them. Set into the corner were shelves and on each were some of the strangest shoes with the highest of heels. How did Madam walk in them? Molly shrugged; clearly it mystified her, too. There was also a metal bustier, made of copper or brass. We exchanged a look – that look a thousand, thousand years old between women about other women, which says much – but neither of us referred to what Madam did for a living.

Next, the bathroom, very pale, wood-lined to halfway up the walls. "Madam was thinking of taking this out," announced Molly for Madam, apparently presently on a plane and not expected back for several days, "as Madam thinks it looks like a ship's bathroom."

"It looks rather nice," I defended the bathroom, "like it should be beside the sea. With a view of the sea at least. I would put up a painting." Molly did not see the joke there.

The bathroom had a bidet – still quite unusual in the mid-eighties. Molly limited herself to "Madam had it put in." Still, neither of us made any reference to Madam's profession. Madam took her phone number, the cats and her clients with her upon departure. Upon moving in, I took the mirrors off the bedroom walls and what there was of the ceiling. You can take voyeurism to extremes. Gerald never commented on their absence and I never quizzed him on how he knew Madam. If I had, doubtless *Business, my Sweet, a business connection* would have been the response.

Surprisingly the flat/shoebox was bought in my name. Do not trouble yourself by thinking how kind this was. In this Gerald, or rather his solicitor Frobisher, of Frobisher, Chapman and Dodd, was discreet. The flat was signed over to me, given to me, in my name because Gerald Wendon-Davis could not let the papers near the potential scandal. I will not linger long over the potential headlines there could have been. See how wise I was becoming. The Sunday papers would have had a field day. *MP's husband's love nest uncovered.* You could just imagine the fuss. It would not have been a good day for Mrs Bright Green Suit. Maybe the press conference would have had to be at the main gates of the estate, not the farm. Perhaps she might have bitten the pink lips then. But no, this was prevented. Gerald paid for it, gave it, yes, gave it to me. Or his solicitor, Mr Frobisher, who was discreet and coughed a lot at the appropriate moments, did. It was his suggestion, the discreet gift. As near as Gerald could come to discretion, by proxy, through the idea of a third party.

The flat is near the river, near Jermyn Street, near the manicurist and Tony the hairdresser, for the hair and the dabbing. What was my function in all this? I never asked. Did the cat get my tongue? Presumably, if Gerald had wanted to, he could have appointments with us all in the same afternoon. I wonder now what I was down as in his diary. In between the Right Hon., and Sir This-That. Was I The Other? Did he come to me first, in order not to ruffle the buffeted locks? Is this too harsh, too bitter? I am letting the side down again, forgetting the good times. And the flat… he did give me the flat.

The location of it is oddly close to the House where Mrs W-D spent her days. And presumably many of her nights, during the interminably long evening sittings. Did he want her to know? The House is within waving distance. I can go out on the balcony, and look west and see the flag at the top of the pole to ascertain whether the House is still sitting. Did he buy it for that? Did it somehow tell him where she was, or should be? I know that it was jolly expensive – how did he hide that? *Oh, lovelies you know, lovelies*, with a wave of the hand. Lovelies is – sorry, was – a Gerald-ism for money. Lovers don't normally talk about money. He was also a good hand-waver. Pictures in the air, like his writing on paper.

The flat faces west. Late afternoons and early evenings in summer, you can sit on the balcony (or indeed the bed) with a glass of chilled, white wine and watch the sun smear itself across the sky, all the shades of red, before it finally succumbs to its lover, gravity, whom it has teased and defied all the day, glowing above Earth. This was Gerald pontificating by the way, it is not my description. Gerald could make anything passionate. With or without a glass of wine in his hand, or an adoring audience to strut before. The glasses on his nose – very dark, very heavy – made him look more professorial, more intellectual. You would have listened. Probably he would have been an excellent estate agent. Not that he would have been described thus. A merchant of quality locations. Or something similar. But only amongst a certain select elite. (Remember, certain – Gerald would be certain of the sale. Select – Gerald had selected the victim. Sorry the purchaser. Elite, well it goes without saying.) Not the hoi polloi. My view of the sun setting from the balcony means the signal for a certain rising smell from the restaurant next door, albeit several floors below, and the outline of the high-rises black against the horizon towards Paddington. Even from my bed I can count the planes stacking as they wait to land at Heathrow. Oh, and the windows have never shut properly, still do not shut properly if the wind is coming from the east. I have said that Gerald did not 'do'; he would not have noticed this, still less have done anything about it.

Before the flat was purchased, to facilitate meetings (meetings!) with Gerald, he would suggest, if we had not met, say, on a Wednesday or a Thursday, that I take up temporary residence en route to High Fold. This sounds so ridiculous now, but remember then I was madly in love, the roses still blooming, the violins hard at it, the bubbles of champagne still rising to the surface of the glass, before 'pop', into oblivion. I was only a junior at the academy of Experience.

So, in the summer of 1983 I was taken up the A12 and introduced to Southwold, that small town on the east coast, which, following his first letter, I had already found on the map. "Very select, Sweeting," said Gerald unnecessarily, for self-evidently it was, but Gerald was still doing the estate agent act. I said nothing, it was not necessary. "So convenient, such a good place to stop over briefly," Gerald mused, glibly, selling the place to me as, for once, we drove up together, for the first time, passing, also en route, the Cathedral of the Marshes at Blythburgh, but of this, this time, hardly a mention. "You'll love it, so discreet, so distinguished," as the lighthouse and the church tower came into view on the horizon.

Of Southwold itself, how could he possibly think the place was discreet? During summer it is full of discerning Londoners, mostly of a particular gene pool and bank account, in the ridiculously, fabulously and apparently famously expensive, all-colours-of-the-rainbow beach huts by the sea. In July and August particularly, it becomes the temporary preserve of discerning journalists with their children, extolling in print the virtues of an 'old-fashioned' English holiday by the sea. At such times, a pairing such as Gerald and I could not be seen together. Imagine the scoop: *MP's husband discovered in...* Name your location; love nest, compromising position (always those) whatever, it would all be the same. The life blood of the red-top Sunday papers. T'was ever thus for such as we. It would certainly have paid for the journalist's family holiday. In winter it hums, as only a close-knit, theatrical, literate, all-knowing community can hum. Father Christmas now arrives at the newly rebuilt pier to a huge crowd that comes for the Christmas lights and the essence of an occasion we all recall from childhood. Over all, when the wind is in the right direction, there is the smell of hops and malt from the brewery. Hops, malt and salt. It is a heady combination.

And the stopovers were brief. He would leave London after lunch on Friday, stop off with me for an hour or so

– remember how practised he was at the quick getaway? Sometimes on such occasions it would be more than the thirty minutes in London. Then washed, dabbed, polished, on he would go to duties at High Fold. The same quite often would work in reverse on Sundays. I did used to wonder how he explained his long journey time away. "Hold-up on the A12," he would murmur absently or "Stick-up in Southwold," as he reached for me, to divert my attention. And we would laugh then, carefree at his ribaldry.

Our first coupling there in that summer of 1983 was in a terraced cottage in the heart of Southwold. "Under the lighthouse," murmured Gerald with a smile, which for Gerald was a subtle but shockingly saucy thing to say. I was quite taken aback. At the subtlety. Most un-Gerald-like. The lighthouse rears up from the cluster of houses around it, white, tall, separate from the land. You can see it for miles. I understood the reference, though by then I was passing the very first flush of passion, a year into the relationship and references to sex were becoming a little wearing. It was a borrowed cottage, from a friend of a friend. Another Gerald presumably, men who connect.

But imagine the pleasure of this, post-coitus, though Gerald would call it other things, dressing, but dressing in a fleece-lined pyjamas-like suit, which I learned to buy more of, all soft and warm against bruised and tender skin, forgoing the wire and elastic of underwear, the constraints of ordinary clothes. Then the joy of having fish and chips burning your fingers, out of the paper, in Gerald's big car, amid those sumptuous leather seats, on the top of the cliff, overlooking the sea. Smiling and laughing the while, feeding each other chips, blowing on our burned fingers, burning our lips with the greed for hot food. "Satisfaction, my Sweet, with every erection," Gerald would remind me, full of post-sexual intimacy, waving a chip at me. Never in high summer, the evenings were too light too late and there was a danger I might be seen in the car with Gerald, but often, often in winter and autumn, when the air was still gentle and the darkness between the lamplights gathering. Then we could be private, safe, no one to see him or the number plate (GAWD 1 – well, of course. Gerald Alexander Wendon-Davis) and I in close proximity. So imagine, your body all warm, aching a little from making love, the scent and the pleasure of chips, all salty, firm, hot, then the fish, wonderful fresh, soft, flaking fish, eaten between your fingers, an hour or so of lovemaking behind you, and all accompanied by the sound of the sea on the pebbles below on the beach. Then after that, Gerald would leave me, kiss me on the nose, drive northwards, as it was Friday, and he was on duty thereafter. But in the gentle dusk of the car, between pools of orange lamplight, the planes of his face were gentled by lovemaking, gentled again by the shadows in the car and for a few more minutes he was all mine. Sometimes I wondered how he got rid of the smell of the chips – presumably he drove on afterward with the windows open. And Gerald liked pickled eggs – even now the thought makes me shudder.

There is always an end to such things and this early supper helped to lessen that loss. And I? I would go back to the cottage and, after a bit, settle to read, with perhaps a glass of wine, sometimes a wonderful mug of tea, then a bath, to ease the ache. And not much later, get into bed, the sheets that strangely luxurious cotton that is hard, yet soft too, all scented from the sea air and wind, and from Gerald's lavender (concocted by Tony); the scene of our lovemaking not long before. And I would sleep the sleep of the unborn and the untroubled, cocooned in Gerald's scent. And love? I have not added love here. Gerald never, over all the years we were together, said 'I love you'. If pressed, he might query "Love you? Of course I do, Sweeting! How ridiculous!" as though I were completely daft to doubt. Then "What's for dinner?" or "How's about another glass of wine?" or something else to divert the temporary surfacing of my insecurities. But he did not say the words, those specific words. And I would console myself, he did love me, he did, he must have done. No one stays with their mistress for so long, do they, for years and years, without loving them? Do they?

I have lost count of the number of times I have now driven the route up the A12, round Ipswich (all those roundabouts), continued through the gently rolling countryside, waiting almost breathless for the sight of the tower at Blythburgh, as the signal for the turn-off to Southwold. Actually I grew to love it, the town itself. More than him? Yes, probably. Over time, the community was kind enough to take me to its heart. The town did not hurt me, leave me high and dry for days and weeks on end, cause me the most appalling heartache, lead me into my older years, high and dry at the end of it all, as the tide moves and merges the waters from the constraining river banks into the wider ocean, leaving me stranded on the banks, beyond the reach of the flowing water. There I did find a society, some kindred spirits, several really very kind-hearted people.

Like him it is true that it makes more of itself than in reality is there. Or its residents do and everyone conspires together, residents and visitors, to preserve the illusion. It is the overhang of an age past, that we all look back to.

Childhood is bathed in an evocative, mellow afternoon light, in a room that is only seldom opened and smells a bit dusty and musty. There may even be the smell of apples, moulding, in that golden warmth. In our childhoods, all the summer days were warm, all the days were happy and long. Through the eyes of my love, till they were opened utterly, he was in love with me, never mind all the unexplained straying. "Business, my Sweeting, a little business," he would rumble if I ever thought to ask. Don't tarry over the question of rejecting Gerald because of all these other women he chased after. There is no point in attempting to change the leopard's spots. It is similar to that old story of teaching a pig to sing. Trying wastes your time and annoys the animal in question. Accept or reject the whole package. What a long way off such days seem now.

I remember I was on the way to Suffolk once of my own accord. It was a blackberry day – a Gerald-ism, one of those days in very late summer, crossing into the first hints of autumn, where the sun is so seemingly warm, lingers so long, but there is strength in neither gesture. And it truly was blackberry time, plus, if one cared to harvest it, a bumper crop of hawthorns too adorning the hedgerows. I had already had a letter from Gerald that week, matching the season, and care of High Fold, along the lines of:

> *Imagine the pleasure of a sun-warmed blackberry, black and luscious, picked with the early morning dew still on the grass underfoot. And the promise still of a hot day already in the sky. Already we are into that season of the sloe, that dusty purple olive of the English hedgerow.*

It is the season of the pleasure of closing the curtains, to keep the darkness out and turning on the lights, pools of warm cosiness. Autumn is my favourite time of the year, the lingering, mature warmth, the mist over dawn, the first shaft of the sun over the barley stubble, the fruits, the smells, all the seed heads and then the coming in, the rediscovery of the pleasure of the warmth of, and need for, wearing wool. Soon we will have fires in the evening and there will be a smell of woodsmoke in the mornings.

Clearly a Mrs W-D-monitored letter. 'We', again. Swirls and loops, loops and swirls. More than a swallow does in a summer. "Read the message behind the lines, Sweeting, read how cosy it all is," he would urge. To Gerald, master in his subject, communication, in whatever guise, was all. Even in dagger form.

This day all that was behind me. I had the whole weekend to myself. Instead of another one of Gerald's friend's convenient cottages, I had found a small B&B to stay in for the weekend, on South Green, in Southwold, very near the sea. I would hear it when I awoke. I was already looking forward to it. The landlady was a very large woman, with a considerable, formidable chest, on which trembled the brooch of the day. She was always properly dressed and whenever I had met her, as on a number of occasions I had had cause to, she had always called out from the depths of the house: "Help yourself to a large gin, dear. I only use it to clean my rings otherwise." My sort of woman, as Gerald might say approvingly. I knew her only as Mrs M. What had happened to Mr M was not made clear. She made you most welcome, as did her Scottie dog, who several times had endeared himself to Gerald on the beach, which was how I had got to know her.

As I drove, I noticed the hedges were even yet black with ripened berries. Gerald's observation was, of course, correct. Had the Devil spat on them yet? Gerald's letter had said, after a certain date, country folk do not pick the berries as the Devil has been by. Not that Gerald went near a blackberry unless it was on a white plate accompanied by clotted cream, all atop a white, linen tablecloth and that beside a glass of something sweeter - but not too sweet - to wash it down. Usually followed by cheese. Very English. "No funny French eating habits here, my sweet," he would say as he plunged a knife into the Stilton. Unless, of course, the guest was French, but my heart cannot dwell long here. French women, Italian too, are far too beautiful, it is in the genes. And Gerald adored them all.

It was the party conference season, mid-September into October. It was just after the MP Alan Clark had died, at the very end of the summer in 1999, and I think the general feeling was that politics from that time would be quieter, less fun. Gerald had liked Alan Clark though he had only known him through the papers; we had had a special dinner together to mark his passing. He thought the MP's caddish ways rather amusing and had read his published diaries with great fervour and much laughter. Gerald had read chunks of them to me with considerable relish, usually after our own tussle between the sheets, in which, Gerald felt Alan Clark would have been proud to be involved, if only via his book.

That weekend I was not seeing Gerald. Or so I thought. Mrs W-D's party was being corralled at Brighton, the party whips marshalling the MPs and their wives into safe hotel rooms and the conference halls. To hear the Word. To applaud. To give the Leader the standing ovation. The press would all be there. At that time, the general thinking amongst the whips used to be that MPs' wives do not run wild and reacted well to being shepherded and then cooped. Sadly, the whips never thought to similarly corral the MPs' husbands, who in party terms were felt generally to be capable of looking after themselves during Conference. If female MPs were a scarce commodity, MPs' husbands were a rare breed indeed. But to direct MPs' husbands in a similar fashion to the wives – how demeaning. Surely MPs' husbands, so limited in number that they were, were all fine upstanding, responsible members of the community. Capable, you could add to this description, of looking after themselves. Behaving themselves. Responsible adults, worthy of the party. It would be insulting to consider them otherwise, so ran the party line. The days of spin and counter-spin, and toeing the party line with the help of the buzz of the pager and the text of the whip were far, far into the future. How things have changed.

It was a lovely day and I turned off the A12 towards Orford, to run down to the quay for a little while, to break the last part of the journey. At the quayside little had changed in thirty-five or so years, since I was a child. There were the usual array of tiny fishing boats and yachts. The curve of shore used as a sort of store for the boats was the usual muddle of bits and pieces for messing by the sea, or so it seemed to my town eyes. On the quay itself there were a few families who had escaped the weekend traffic early. Weekenders, whose children were the usual middle-class, well-polished variety seen all over East Anglian coasts, all with their crab catchers and their buckets. As a child, I did this, with my brothers when we went on holiday. Several generations of one family come together to concentrate their whole beings on capturing small, encrusted animals, with wavy arms and a powerful nip, and keeping these, albeit temporarily, in brand-new plastic buckets, purchased specially for the occasion. The ritual is the same in every place; it is always the parent who is anxiously surveying the depths, waving the line into it, enticing the inhabitants with mysterious things as bait. And the children are all perched, bottoms upwards, on the quayside, either gazing downwards, with a strong risk that they may pitch forward at any second into the water, or into the bucket at their victims.

Indeed as I settled then, beside the sea, on a bench in the sun, the very last of the summer wine, a very small boy and his mother came along. It was apparently her intention to take the last of the sun and the excuse was that she would teach him how to catch crabs. The small boy was called something like Justin and was wearing a life jacket, which I thought was a brilliant idea, though 'Mummy' was very keen on keeping him away from the water. "What's a crab, Mummy?" kept punctuating the air, whilst she unloaded the crab rods, the bucket, they found a stone (for unspecified use), loaded the bacon onto the rod… And then she looked at Justin and said, in tones that conveyed much inside information, "You want a wee wee, don't you?" Justin was having none of this and questions about crabs still followed, over and over. "This is the deal," she said. "We'll go and you do a wee wee and we'll get your cardigan as it is cold by the water (this on a day where the temperature was still in the high twenties) and when we come back there will be loads of crabs." Off they went. This I had to see. And verily, when Justin and his mum came back, settled down the cardigan, pulled up the crab line… lo, there was a champion crab, munching away on his next meal. What a great mum! And Justin learned what a crab was, including much later, how fast they move – sideways of course – except that he had to be stopped from stamping on it and in loud tones he decided that he did not like them, though he did like the excitement of catching them. Mummy proved an expert catcher, including picking them up off the quayside when they tried to get away.

My attention drifted away. The wind lifted my hair, took the cobwebs from my brain. A whole weekend to myself, I mused, without Gerald running in and out, like a bookend, punctuating Friday and Sunday and compressing the bit in between so that I would be always alert, always ready for him. The bench was warm. The air was sweet. An old lady and her daughter came to sit beside me, shielding me slightly from the breeze, and on the other side were a foursome, two married couples, the children long fled the nest, enjoying as I, the late sun, the fresh air, the smell of the sea, the children playing over the buckets, the welcome rest from normal labours.

There was a very lovely, old-fashioned boat in front of the quay, the kind I would, in other circumstances, imagine sailing in the Caribbean, with lashings of rum and beautiful men and girls with very deep tans. A team of very smartly dressed people kept lovingly tending it, each of them wearing the ship's name – the *Geraldine* – embroidered on their T-shirts, and they were utterly and transparently in love with her; each member of her crew polishing and caressing her. She was taking most of the quayside up, but her crew clearly took this position as of right. She was so beautiful, it was only seemly. She was queen of all she surveyed.

I was fascinated by the crab collections, but, after a long time, I began to realise that four or perhaps five very garrulous, older men had arrived alongside the *Geraldine*, after – as they informed, in very loud and well-spoken tones, anyone who would listen – an excellent lunch at the Crown and Castle just nearby, off the market square. I suppose, if I had stopped to really look at them, I would have recognised the type. Gerald's H&Hs – the Hail and Hearties – the City types whose waistlines expand with their bank accounts and expense accounts and their tailoring. But my mind was elsewhere, on the children, on the crabs, on the warmth of the late summer sun.

It was the sound of giggling that distracted me back to the boat, that and the glitter of metal catching the sun. A collection of girls, well, good-time girls, working girls more likely from their gab and all the sun-glaring jewellery, were moving towards the *Geraldine*. This was not what I had had in mind in my scenario in the Caribbean. They were very out of place on the quayside, on such a late summer's day, amidst the holidaymakers. Amid bleached cotton, wind-tanned skin, baggy clothes, bare toes, the innocent pursuit of crab fishing, they clashed with their bright, cropped, tight clothes hugging each curve, accentuating every asset. Heavily made-up and sprayed, they giggled, tottered, clattered their way on board, the hellos boomed towards them by the H&Hs, their high-pitched returning hellos twittered back. Presumably the whole party had lunched together. They all seemed like old friends, well, friends whose acquaintance was longer than a few minutes. Certainly there was no shyness in their chatter. Perhaps it was the effect of the alcohol at lunch.

If there was a discrepancy in the women's clothes and the location, so there was in age between the H&Hs and the women. Did I notice then, or was it just an irritant, only something that registered later, when the soothing effect of the sun and the water and the innocence of the children had faded from memory? Certainly some of the girls were youngish, early twenties, very full of that confidence and bloom that travels well on young skin but fades with the onset of age. It is a look and a feel that manufacturers of skin cream aspire to in their dreams, knowing it for just that, a dream, if you are long in the glare of the sun, publicity, chemicals, stress, or your heart is broken too often. It is the dream that fades with the tick of the clock. Not all the girls were that young. Some of them were older. They had the look. That look that comes from dancing too close to the flame. The older women had begun to know of those two partners, Rejection and Disappointment, who come with time.

Just then another larger boat was cutting its way upstream on the tide and turning to dock, to let off the cargo of fish the quay had been designed for, as opposed to the *Geraldine*'s still-growing cargo of City types, intent on a good time. On land, the girls giggled, the men guffawed, clapped each other on the back as H&Hs do. What was holding up departure? The fishing boat began the turn into the tide to come alongside and moor.

Passengers for the *Geraldine* – more men, some girls – were still arriving. The men on the fishing boat, the *Joanna* (named for someone's wife, someone's daughter?) were holding her back, riding the incoming tide, tired and impatient at the frivolities on the quayside. But even I, with my townie eyes, could see that the *Joanna* could not moor properly as the *Geraldine*, with her loud and flashy cargo, was taking up too much space. Still the *Geraldine* did not leave.

A sense of immediacy begins to imbue the proceedings. The *Joanna* cannot wait. The tide is carrying her back, she cannot hold the hover on the water, waiting, waiting, waiting to dock. She comes to moor alongside the quay. It is very tight, and that smartly crewed and labelled crew on the *Geraldine* are asked, via shouts over the speeding water, to move forward. The tide is still coming in, and the *Geraldine* moves forward into it. Unbelievably, passengers for the *Geraldine* are still arriving. How many are there? Difficult to say, but seemingly about a dozen. Perhaps more. People are holding ropes, manoeuvring the *Geraldine* forward, alongside, forward again. One of the H&Hs is still on the quayside, holding a rope. There is much shouting and yelling, directions, instructions loosed on to the wind, to be lost and repeated amongst the crowd of children and parents still trying to fish for crabs on the quay.

Eventually, someone who is not going on the *Geraldine* comes forward and replaces the passenger on the quayside, who then swings his leg over and gets on board. He is greeted as a long-unseen friend, with claps and cheers. But hark, there is one more… even as the *Geraldine* is catching the current, beginning to swing unperceived, borne on the incoming tide, ever, ever so slightly into a ninety-degree turn away from the quayside. The final passenger-to-be throws the rope from the front of the ship and, as his arm releases it, it flies through the air; it seems to flash into consciousness, like a photograph, snaking into the sky. Inexplicably, fleetingly, I am reminded of the swirls and whirls of Gerald's writing. Writ large across the sky. Black-inked script against the cream paper.

The last man, still on *terra firma*, begins to run, to follow the rope. I can see movement in amongst the muddle of people at the end of the quay. So he runs, and runs. And leaps. And reaches for the ship's rail. The ninety-degree turn of the boat away from the quay becomes more pronounced. The *Geraldine* is moving away. He is still leaping. There is a silence. All you can hear is the wind as his leap curves against the pull of the earth. Like the stills of a film, stark, movement, up, up, across… And he falls, falls, falls. Falls short. Falls into the sea. Splash! Like an arrow, like a dart, straight into the water.

From the quayside, like a football crowd at a goal, as one we leap to our feet and gasp. Time stops.

There is a time frame to women's lives, tempered by their reproductive system. First there is the onset of periods, which runs naturally into producing babies/not producing babies for whatever reason, bringing up a family or not, then the menace/relief of the ticking biological clock. Later, there is the menopause. For men, there is not this demarcation of time, no changes wrought within their bodies effect their outer lives in anything like the same inexorable way. For men, there comes the time they are taller than their fathers, then they are capable, strong, invincible, in their own minds, if no one else's. Age brings the unpleasant reality home, that they are no longer tall enough, strong enough, fit enough. As the man crashed into the drink, did this reality come home then?

But I digress. Time has slowed in the man's rise, hung in mid-air as he went through the arc of his leap, sped on as he fell dart-like into the sea. From those seconds of silence, where only the wind heard your heartbeat as the man tried desperately to hold back the years, to cling to the air, suddenly the whole scene has sprung back to life. On land, we all turn and clutch each other. We jabber and point "Did you see, did you see?" and as one we all lean over the quayside. On the water, there is much scrabbling on the *Geraldine*. "Man overboard," the cry goes up. Yes really – I thought they only did that in stories. And a rope goes down. The man in the water comes up for air, grabs the rope and – in what seems a long time, but is really only seconds – is bodily lifted by one of his co-travellers out of the water. He is still wearing his glasses. Rather as you might imagine Eric Morecambe if he was playing the scene.

In fact, he is much the same as he was before he went in, except utterly drenched. The shirt is no longer crisp. Mr George of Savile Row would not recognise the trousers, now dripping. The hair, the mane, is glued to his face, a vision normally only seen by Tony of Jermyn Street. No scent of lavender now, more *Eau d'Estuaire* and that on the fishy side. The planes across his cheeks are taut from the effort in his arms, to grasp the rope. Never has he held onto a woman like he is holding onto that rope, even in his wildest most youthful moments, now so many years behind him. The man who thought he was still young, still lithe, still capable of jumping an ever-widening gap of water, to land cat-like (in his dreams) on the boat, was, of course, Gerald. You naturally have arrived at this, long before me. I should have realised. Even from the name of the boat, but an extension of his narcissism, though there must be a thousand such ships so named. The crowd at that end of the quay had hidden him from me. How could I not have known?

The urgency had gone from the day. The boat completed its ninety-degree turn on the tide and, just for good measure, indeed as a kind of finale to the proceedings, smacked into the *Joanna*, before the current carried it upstream. The *Joanna*, clearly a sturdy craft and used to knocks and blows, rode the attack as the *Geraldine* moved away. I wish I could say that Gerald had fallen in the gap near the rear part of the boat – that the propeller caught his arm or something and the sea was suddenly red, like in *Jaws*, but of course it was not like that. Gerald could survive anything and smell of roses, he just could not walk on water. My cynicism interferes. There was Gerald, in his favourite position, the centre of all attention, albeit that he was lying on the walkway of the boat; even the captain of the *Geraldine* seemed to have left his bridge. The shame of it. After all, the bills were paid by the man prone on deck, who had just been fished out of the water. The captain obviously needed to know his boss was still breathing.

I suppose, looking back, I should have been upset, worried, at the prone man on the deck. Surrounded by all those men, the captain of his ship, and all those women… Perhaps this was the start of the anger, the blatant womanising beginning to affect me. I don't know now. I saw him lift his head as the boat began to reappear upstream of the *Joanna*. He was alive. That was all I needed to know, then. Already I could hear his soothing tones: *Business, Sweeting, a little business, that's all. It meant nothing else.* That conversation would be private. His public dip into the sea would not be the end of the matter.

For of course there was more. Someone on the quayside had a video, to record the crabbing, but as luck would have it, used judiciously to record much of the incident. It was on the news, suitably cut. Stills from it were relayed to the evening news. News was quiet from the conference floor in Brighton. Indeed, Gerald had often remarked that life was quieter without Mrs Thatcher and after her departure the men in grey suits took over. With Alan Clark also gone, things became even quieter. I can never think of John Major without the link to peas, as depicted in that programme then fashionable, *Spitting Image*, or William Hague without the cartoon nappy idea. You can see how the newsrooms leapt collectively with delight at Gerald's mishap. Next day's papers carried the headline, *MP's husband rescued from the drink*, which in the circumstances I did chuckle over. There he was, coming out of the water, all the water pouring off him, the knuckles welded white around the rope, the glasses in situ. I noticed tartly over breakfast the following day, as I pored over the article, that there was no reference to the women on the boat, no thundering headline, *MP's husband associated with floating bordello*. At last, the party whips had presumably, finally, caught up with the stable door, though as ever the horse had bolted. I also wondered just what small print had Gerald been trying to read or had the glasses, vainly rejected for so long other than to look professorial, at last become a constant necessity?

The real victim in all this, poor individual, was not there at all, even to relish the Schadenfreude of her husband's embarrassment. No, when I first fell in love with her husband, I never thought I would say this, but poor Mrs Wendon-Davis. She, wearing but the latest in a line of bright-green suits, was far away, suitably corralled, penned and hemmed in at Brighton. Red-faced against the green presumably when she heard the news and heard the reaction. About the time the Leader should have been headline news for the latest ovation at Conference, in newspaper offices across the country Gerald's picture was replacing it on the front page of that evening's papers. After all, the Leader always gets an ovation. There is always a rather churlish note of the timing of the length of the ovation and sometimes, a particularly churlish comparison to other party leaders who have gone before, notably by then, with Maggie's finest hours. But this day, on more than one newspaper and certainly amongst the red tops, the ovation moved to page two, the reader directed to it by a small heading on the front page. Centre-stage was Gerald clutching the rope, white knuckles well visible on the cord. Mrs W-D was hauled up, rather as her husband had been, hers not from a ducking, but to a mauling. A hauling to a mauling, like a playground rhyme.

It was not Gerald's finest hour, it was not good for Mrs W-D, but it afforded me a certain specific Germanic pleasure.

10

The Woman Before Me

Have I mentioned that there was another mistress before me? Has this fact been self-evident? I have innocently mentioned that at times Gerald went away, without any explanation from him whence he went or with whom. Remarkable now, looking back, that in the early days, I did not query it. As my mother would say: "To the pure, all things are pure." Sometimes as I have said, he might arrive with one lady, leave with another. Presumably news of a mistress before me comes as no surprise to anyone else. Extraordinary though it may seem, it never occurred to me before I knew, that there had been. But really, thinking on it, I am not sure now, knowing all that I know, why I was surprised. But I was. And Gerald – Gerald who can apparently pass a woman he has spent the night with, without even looking at her a second time as he does so – never thought to warn me. Or indeed, presumably, her. What Gerald gave so he could take away, his love, his time, his affection. This may be acceptable for the one-night stand – though my heart still goes out to Ascot Girl for that awful moment that morning at the underground station, which I know she will never forget – but for a mistress? Amongst thieves, is that honourable?

Gerald's flat was situated, conveniently, halfway between the West End and the City. Mrs W-D apparently resided during the week in a tiny flat nearer to Westminster and the magnetic pull of the divisional bells in the House. Gerald called her flat the cupboard, or in more witty moments, or so he fancied, 'the closet', as in 'coming out of, Sweeting', as if I needed telling. This arrangement apparently suited her working hours, in the years long before the House began to think about moving to more regular timekeeping early in the new century. The closet joke was one of the few Gerald made about his wife. We never discussed their living arrangements otherwise – why should we have done, it was another relationship, not one I wanted to know much about either. However, his flat, a more spacious affair, was in the Barbican development, in one of the towers, from whose westward-facing balcony he truly did have magnificent views of the sun setting. I did not go there very often. My flat, as I have said, was near the Haymarket, right in the middle of theatre land.

One of our favourite occupations together was to walk. Very often Gerald would accompany me back to my flat, strolling in the evening air, not hand in hand as lovers, but arm in arm companionably seemed acceptable to anyone watching. To Gerald, London was his capital, his territory, his domain. He regarded it as a king might his land.

By day, the streets are the province of the grey-suited men, black-suited women. Latterly, from about the mid-nineties, I have noticed that the women have taken to wearing longer jackets, so that as they move and the breeze picks up the cloth, they look like bats airing their wings. Mobile phones now abound everywhere, lining strained, usually young, pale faces. Sometimes I have walked across the concourse at Liverpool Street Station and played the game of counting the number of people on the phone within a space that must only be about some five hundred yards across. Sometimes I have counted up to thirty or forty faces, now of course, many more, anxiously working the phone. Everyone is anxious in London.

There are the huge, red, lumbering buses, elongated coaches, traffic wardens, lorries, delivery vans, taxis turning on a sixpence. In darkened doorways where the wind cannot reach, workers gather to suck on cigarettes, leaving the white butts abandoned underfoot, compressed, waiting to be swept up, the spaces made clean. Everywhere there are now CCTV cameras ("accursed things" – Gerald); nowhere now are there the private, intimate spaces, where fleetingly some sexual comfort may be sought and given, the exchange unseen by security men watching little televisions from the comfort of a warm, lit office.

Everyone has 'carry out bags', or 'bag meals'. Gerald frequently scoffed at this and then bewailed the passing of lunch. "Does no one have time for the art of lunching, Sweeting?" Gerald, probably a man born after his time, bemoaned the advent of the twenty-first century coming to London. "What is the City coming to? How can a man do decent business? It is all so fast – there is no time to consider!" he would rail, seeing another cluster of bags being clutched as the owner hurried back to his or her desk to eat. "As my old granny would say," this delivered by Gerald with a twinkle, "they hardly know how to live a minute!" Privately, even in the beginning, I often doubted that Gerald had an old granny, or that she had said such a thing, but to him I would just nod and smile. Gerald was not from the stock that has grannies. The generation before his parents had nicknames or formal names, but in our relationship they were seldom referred to. Obliquely, I was given to understand that the family name had come down but not the money. But I digress…

Latterly, Gerald would ring me sometimes and decry his lunch. "Do you know what we ate for lunch, Sweeting? Sushi! How's a man supposed to survive on raw fish! What is London becoming, an invasion of coffee shops and sushi bars!" Taken by a client, or better still a potential client, of course Gerald publicly loved sushi. Chameleon Gerald, in public and in bed, keeping up what he believed was an appearance of modernity. Gerald would intone to his clients one of his mottos: "Spot a trend before it spots you." And everyone would nod sagely, but rarely the wiser.

Over the years, buildings have mushroomed up amid the cranes, some so fast it is seemingly overnight. A building was demolished, the site cleared, the diggers move in, the cranes are aloft, the new skeleton arises. Gerald loved all this. "My city," he would proclaim, standing by the window of his flat, high above the London streets, "my city." So proud; "See, Sweeting, see it never sleeps, always changing." High up there, you could always see lines of traffic moving, along all the lit streets, London is never still, even in the small hours. This was long before Mayor Livingstone's congestion charge, when during the day the roads were clogged and traffic crawled at nineteenth-century horse-powered speed. There was always a hum, even up there on his balcony, and inside when the windows were shut. And always as we walked, seeking highways, byways and back-ways, across squares and gardens, the Inns of Court, there was the hum, constant, more constant than a heartbeat, more constant than breathing. "These new buildings," contemptuously Gerald would wave his chubby hand dismissively as we walked by the Old Bailey into Fleet Place, a place so new in the late-nineties for months it hardly appeared on maps (one of Gerald's solicitor contacts worked there and bikes had a hard time finding the office), "so American, so devoid of style or thought." Gerald was appalled by these new buildings, for all that during the week he lived in what amounted to a seventies tower block, albeit a very expensive one. Location to Gerald (that estate agent in him again) was what counted.

Walking through the City, especially at night, is a strange, otherworldly pursuit. By night, the hum of traffic, though still there, is no longer punctuated or accompanied by the noise of the constant building works. Nothing rests in London ever; there is never a time when the whole City sleeps. The lighted offices at the corporate lawyers scattered around St Paul's make an eternal day, the night sky around Sir Christopher Wren's finest monument is perpetually orange. It is a time for the invasion of the army of cleaners, presumably working around the lawyers, the army of suppliers topping up and replenishing for the return of daylight. And even at night, the swarms of motorbikes that amass the day's streets, are there still, the bikers moored temporarily outside offices, the leather-clad rider waiting for a document, a photograph, a parcel, to whisk it off to another fully lit, fully functioning office, populated by other people shunning sleep or social lives. At night, too, if the lights were on in the older buildings, Gerald would point to the upper rooms, where very often you could see wonderful and huge chandeliers, the ornate plaster work casting shadows around the ceilings. There are always dinners going on, at Mansion House amid all the spectacular flower arrangements with the Lord Mayor, or ceremonies at the Guildhall or in the patterned square in front of it, long limousines parked outside anyhow, awaiting their passengers to finish the evening and arouse the driver. This was Gerald's City, not that of the mobile phone and the all-night working. "Leave that for the lawyers," he would say, with a wondering smile.

One evening in the early summer, so we walked, and in the time before darkness takes over, such as it can in such a populated place via the orange dusk that suffices for night, before the workers make their way home, many cluster, particularly on fine evenings outside wine bars and pubs, making a party of the pavement. I am not sure, but I think this must have been some time in the summer of 1984; certainly, it was comparatively early in our relationship. Was it about the time of the Tube strikes in London? Possibly, which might explain our walking, though Gerald liked to walk sometimes.

That evening, I remember we had stopped by Greyfriars, the ruins of a church just in the shadow of St Paul's, the church tower still standing, a garden marking the outline of the original aisle, the columns, where these had been destroyed during the war. Gerald had been waltzing me round, he humming something very off-key to accompany our steps, through the darker side of the aisle away from the road, looking as though to all the world, we were just larking about. Steadying then, we came to the pavement and walked on, giggling at our silliness.

There was such a cluster of drinkers at the wine bar ahead of us. As we approached, something made me turn from

Gerald's eyes laughing into mine, I remember him patting my hand looped over his arm, still chuckling. There was a movement amid the people in front of us, outside a wine bar. Then a break in the crowd, like a parting of the water, the branches in a forest… the crowd's laughter and chatter began to die. Heads turned.

She stood, as if a deer, caught mid-shock, steadying herself on her ankles. Gloriously high, elegant shoes, a deep, deep green. And she so elegant too, older, an older lady than normally seen in the City now, older but so beautiful, her hair blonde into white, swept up into a chignon, her face beautifully made-up, fine, so fine, high cheek bones, the suit, well cut, also a dark, dark green. And a gold, looped brooch, high on her lapel, a velvet lapel. The longest of necks supporting the chignon. I drew in breath.

A long time ago when I was at school there used to be a lot of bullying, which took place in a kind of protective circle on the adjacent playing fields. The circle gathered out of curiosity and that strange, human desire to see pain inflicted on another, serving too to keep out unwanted prying eyes for a short time. Before hostilities broke out, there would always be a silence, where the protagonists, presumably having seen it on television with professional boxers, would stare each other out against the background of a deep silence. Such a silence was here now. There is something different about the silence of a crowd. The rumble of conversation dies away, ebbs from consciousness. The centre is silent, that silence grows like fog moving noiselessly until you become trapped in your immediate area, surroundings indiscernible, the blur of faces meshing into nothingness. You become faintly aware of other things; on this occasion a taxi hooting, someone shouting, a lorry changing gear, the 'whiff' sound of air brakes, but all these things are distant from you, as the silence grows and deepens. I could hear Gerald's breathing and someone's tummy rumbled. But it becomes the silence you are listening to, fearful of what happens when it is broken. Then you become aware of a persistent beat, a regular one that grows into a thunderous roar. Afterwards you recognise it as your heartbeat, but only after it has thundered, raced and quietened back to normality. As sound and life are resumed, and the fear recedes.

It was, of course, a flash of time that I thought of all that. In those seconds of surveying her, she was transformed. Her head turned, like a bird of prey's, through a ninety-degree circle, to get a proper look after the initial shock. And her eyes began to narrow, catching Gerald in her sights, locking on to him. I could almost hear the wind under her wings, then the start of the scream of her dive.

"So, Gerald," she drew herself up, her voice deep for a woman, very well spoken. Gerald paused, so we paused, rather clumsily on my part and I half-stumbled as I had hardly any warning. Loosened thus, I was immediately at a disadvantage but that was of no consequence in the exchange to come. "Hello, Grace," said Gerald. Not 'Hello there and how are you?' Not a friendly tone. Not a welcome tone. He did not effect the introduction. There was a silence again, like a pebble in water, the ripple expanding from us.

From a great height, she looked at him, not at me. Raising an eyebrow, "Not another one, Gerald surely… another victim? How long before this one suffers?" she sneered, rather spoiling the elegance. She balanced from one foot to the other, her hands twisting around the stem of her glass. She had those overmanicured nails older women have, that become rather talon-like as they thicken, rebuffed constantly by the filing. I was frightened; she was intimidating. "No, Grace, not a victim," responded Gerald, as though I was not there. Grace? Then, she did something so strange, out of keeping for her stature and style. With a flourish, she lifted her glass and threw what was left inside it at Gerald. The contents of a practically full glass, it was very quick, some of it hit me. The bulk of it fell down Gerald, red wine bespattering the suit, a light-grey one, a gold tie and the white shirt. Gerald exclaimed, "What the…" jumping back in sheer reaction. The stain of it oozed into the cloth; there was a very strong smell of wine suddenly abroad on the evening air. There was a quiet; if it is possible, a very loud quiet. He said nothing then; looking at her, she was ablaze with passion, not a hair out of place, her lips compressed with anger, immaculate even then. But nothing was said, nothing. The silence bellowed between them.

Gerald, looking at the suit, let down his arm, so my hand was released. He took out the ubiquitous perfectly folded handkerchief and dabbed at his face, where wine had begun to drip off his cheeks. Putting it away, the stains spreading into the cloth, he bowed ever so slightly as though the bout was complete and it was the required etiquette when a glass of wine has been chucked over you in public by a stunningly elegant woman. Moving his arm behind my back, he ushered me forward and away.

As we moved away, the crowd broke out in hubbub, people laughing, exclaiming, an explosion of sound. We hurried on, his arm guiding me, propelling me indeed, till the noise of the wine bar had subsided and the traffic hum had reasserted itself. I felt blinded with embarrassment, confusion. We stumbled on in silence. I knew who she was, as if a plane had zoomed across the night sky, with a huge advert behind it. A voice in some remote part of me, realising the relationship, wondered whatever had he seen in me?

I babbled at Gerald: "What was all that about?" He ploughed on, smiling, but not in his eyes at first. He was very angry.

"Someone I used to know. Nobody important. She has been – that is, she was – a friend," was all he would say. Then later, as we parted: "Just a little business matter, Sweeting, someone who lost." Can you hear my innocence; can you see it on the page? Who on earth, you may ask, would accept such an explanation? And now there is the answer, I was she apparently; no other explanation was offered, none sought.

Next day, no picture, there had been no flashes, but the Londoner's Diary in the *Standard* carried a paragraph. And that confirmed my realisation.

The paragraph said: *Is it possible the erstwhile, seemingly undividable friendship of Gerald Wendon-Davis and Grace Porterlee is no more? Close friends for more than ten years – he the publicist, she the theatrical lawyer – does this explain his no-show at her recent fiftieth birthday party, celebrated with such panache, at the Savoy? Friends tell us she is devastated at the breakdown between them, which has proved so handy on so many public occasions. Is it possible age has withered their friendship? Furthermore, we understand wine passed between them in the City last night, unhampered by the confines of a glass or bottle and that a bill for dry cleaning a suit may be the final public exchange between this one-time staple of the City social scene.*

There. Quite. Mr Frederick, or Fred, one of Gerald's drivers, tried to trail more of the story, before Gerald obtained the injunction on the Sunday paper that was going to produce all of it.

Remember that Fred? wrote Gerald to me. (*The one that I hate, that passes for what can only be called a sperm donor – as he clearly has no other role in parenting his offspring? Well, he's tried to do the dirty on me. Unthinkable. No standards.* Even in dire circumstances, Gerald would not let that infringement of what he clearly saw as his former chauffeur's parental responsibility go. Gerald, not a father himself, for all his faults took parenthood very seriously. Look at what he did for Greg… but there, I get ahead of myself again.

Funny really, on reflection, that there was no reference to me, as quite clearly I had been with him; we had been laughing together just before the incident. I did wonder if Gerald had pulled strings to keep me out of the story. A long time later, in Gerald's office, I was retrieving a shoe from under the sofa, just before we went out somewhere… I have forgotten now. Instead of the shoe, I pulled out a photograph frame and there were the two of them, he and she, at some function, amid a mass of others, smiling. The message was clear. They were not smiling for the camera. Indeed I wonder if at the second the picture was taken they were even aware the photographer was there. He has his arm part-way round her waist. Her lips are parted. She had signed the photograph, *Dear* GAWD, *a truly great evening! Love, the DG.* I put the photo frame back, without saying a word. It was not difficult to work out Gerald's name for her. Sometimes I would find him doing the crossword. "Sweeting, five down, two words, quotidian prayer, clever, eh?" In my mind's eye, I could picture him as he undressed her (see, there are no hiding places when you are jealous), muttering in that intimate space between lovers, *Give us this day our daily grace*, and her smiling, the Daily Grace, I could picture her smiling their shared, private, intimate smile. And his response. Or another thought, Gerald: *Give me my orders, Director General.* Shaking my head to dispel the picture, I found the shoe. I did not want to think of her desolation. All that happiness, according to the snide paragraph in the paper, now dumped. There but for the grace of God – see, even then her name precedes the thought, just as she had preceded me.

And think how obvious it was. Of course. Hindsight again. Gerald and she had been lovers – she, well, his mistress really, since for Gerald lovers seemed to come and go sometimes on a daily basis. Why had it not occurred to me before? The day after Ascot, for example, when I had assumed Gerald had gone off the night before with that girl, the one I saw on the Underground, he turned up all beautifully clean and tidy. Befuddled as I was that morning, upset as I had been after that terrible night, even I had noted the pristine shirt, the newly applied aftershave, the crease in the trousers. So he may have spent the evening with Ascot Girl, but presumably he had gone to this Grace person's flat for the night. And then the next day he had come to me, his next victim, his next course, to be collected.

And now it seemed that he had dumped her, without warning, apparently for a younger model, the delights of taut flesh, taut but supple, willing, able. Leaving her the shame of the role, the discarded, older woman. Am I too harsh on him? Don't I have a right? It seemed so shocking.

Would this happen to me?

11

Gerald's Humanity

It would seem that I have made something of a monster of Gerald in these pages, a sexual, predatory monster. But that is not wholly the man I loved, and I should take care to be fairer in putting my record of him down.

He was a very affectionate man and loyal, in his way, which I add before anyone splutters over the term. He was loyal after a fashion, he looked after me for what seems now, like a lifetime, now that, well, what has happened has happened, but was in reality, longer than most modern marriages. And he was very loving, very stable, very generous. I have said he was generous with Mrs W-D's money – which he was – but he tried also to be generous with his time. If he could not be there, he would try to send someone else along, or flowers and a note, scented petals and black swirls, a combination to let you know he was thinking of you, even if he was detained elsewhere. Once I was having a series of moles removed, three of them on the top of my right hip, a tiny operation really, and Marcus turned up, with the then big car, I remember only that it was dark blue, to bring me home afterwards amid what could only be described as an entire hothouse of roses. It was January 1993, I remember the papers were full of an affair John Major was supposed to be having with a woman who cooked occasional dinners at No.10. The real affair he did apparently have, would not be revealed for over a decade. A spread of the newspapers were over the back seat; Gerald had apparently insisted they were there "in case you wanted to see them", Marcus explained helpfully from the front seat. The headlines told the story. I did not need to read the small print to get the more salacious details of an alleged relationship that turned out to be complete fabrication, though Gerald would pore over them. That day, the print rather whirled before my still rather anaesthetised eyes; the car was full of the smell of leather, Gerald's aftershave, some of Marcus's (it being before he changed it) and the roses. The thought was marvellous, very kind, but the combination of scents sickening on top of the anaesthetic. Marcus was kind enough to stop several times on the way home. One must record the practicalities as well as the ridiculous.

The note on the roses said: *I have always enjoyed losing myself in your Bermuda triangle but if the points of it must go, so be it.* The paper is yellowing slightly now; I keep it with the press cuttings that tracked our years together, as well as all the letters. The letters have a blue ribbon around them. Perhaps I should tuck the note in with them. I blush when I see those words now, it was such a Gerald-ese joke but he meant well and the note goes on to tell me to get well, albeit without the moles. And that he would be with me soon, and so he was. Briefly.

And the letters! Well, there are bundles of them. He set such faith by this mode of communication and he was assiduously careful to keep in touch. I have mentioned his letters so often. He prided himself that he followed in Churchill's footsteps, the difference being that I was his mistress, not his wife. I don't know or care to know how the W-Ds communicated. For my part, a letter might arrive every day for a week and perhaps a few days might pass before the next came. It might have been old-fashioned in an increasing electronic age but nonetheless the letters came. He wrote of anything that came into his mind, often quite poetically, and I came to know Norfolk through his eyes.

The spring is here at last! How heart-aching lovely Norfolk is, those lovely mellow old red Elizabethan bricks, of all patterns in the gable ends of listed farmhouses and barns, and over all are strewn daffodils, yellow lining hedges and stone walls and under trees. There were pheasants everywhere and moorhens ducking under the hedges, having survived the shooting season and the road respectively. How shy they are. The sun was a huge glow and everywhere as dust came was pink and full of hope. You would have loved it.

I have masses of such thoughts, written down, tied in ribbon, yellowing now. Funny how the letter itself as a mode of communication has become a thing of the past for today's communicators but yet such a collector's item at auction now. What will the biographers of the future use to pad out their books if all communication is sent via email or, even more transitory, text message? Letters are bulky, messy, they take up space. They are rather like suitcases. We entrust our most private thoughts in them, release them into the world, in such flimsy objects. Onto a sheet of paper, into an envelope go our thoughts and dreams and cheques, birthday cards, best wishes, bills. And then we put them into the public domain, sheathed in just a bit of paper to protect them, as they are jostled about, thrown, packed, dropped, by many different hands, till finally they arrive at their destination, to be slit open, or torn and the contents, if they are still inside, are pulled out. The letter, at best, may be saved, reread, the creases smoothed, the contents cherished. At worst, the letter may be ripped up, burned, used to catch coffee stains… or worse, lost.

The worst form of letter of them all, that I recall Gerald railing against, would be the round robin – produced semi en masse, telling people your news but not asking about them. The once-a-year letter writer, the haven't we done well? Not the tell me about you, how are you, how are your family, how have you fared? Not the do write back and tell. Gerald would rant that the round-robin letter says of its writer he or she is not interested in your response. You do not respond to a round robin, other than to say to other recipients 'did you get it?' and both Gerald and I would sit glumly, contemplating some of the letter's low points. Stories about children you have never met, let alone having to look at the photo the letter may have enclosed. A tale of how well someone's job is going, when in truth you rather hoped the whole project had crashed. Gerald, an utterly addicted and inveterate letter writer, would dismiss the round robin, waving the latest example in his manicured fingers, thrashing it through the air, comparing the contents to the Sunday driver, taking the car out, upsetting the natural established pattern of the road – something special to only be used periodically, without practice or style or finesse.

Gerald wrote of all sorts of things, pages and pages, sometimes whilst in a meeting, often from the car whilst Marcus was driving, easing the car to a halt beside some country postbox, for Gerald to post the envelope. He always had pen and paper with him, just in case a stray thought came to him, that he needed to send to me. I became the recipient of his thinking process. And he was careless with his thoughts. Anyone could have intercepted that post. And see again, what I could have done with some of that information but never did. Funny, but it was not a thought I even entertained. And still he wrote. Of course, I threw nothing away. The bin-searching of the famous that began during the nineties was over a decade away when the first letter came but Gerald was safe. None of his letters were ever found in my bin. Perhaps he sensed that.

He was a very human man, who gave his heart, not only to every lovely girl (and as I grew older they seemed to grow increasingly younger, or is that just policemen?) but to his family, one of whom numbered Max. This was a small black Scottie dog, who lived at High Fold. Gerald would chuckle many Sundays en route back to London via his bookend visitation to my weekends in Southwold when he was telling me how, the previous Friday, Max had cannoned down the hall to him, and jumped into his arms, oh, sweet joyous reunion after a week, sometimes more, apart. And Max would shadow him all weekend, presumably just as the young Greg had done at the fete all those summers past, the light of absolute adoration in his twinkly black eyes. Just like Greg's young blue eyes. At the end of the weekend, Max would sit on the gravel and watch Gerald's car go down the drive, till it was out of sight. Gerald said that most Fridays, if it was not the hallway they met in, Max would be sitting on the drive waiting for the car to arrive. And as he recounted this, Gerald would shake his head at such love, such anticipation, such sheer loyalty. Other people carry photos of their wives in their wallets or, at the very least, their children. Well Gerald had Max. He did not have children and he could hardly have a picture of me there.

Thus if Max was effectively Gerald's child though not in so many words, then how could I possibly be jealous of a dog? It was all the more heartbreaking then when one Thursday the letter came. Gerald's script. Very black ink.

> *Max Wendon-Davis – 6th December 1985 to 27th February 2001 – left us on Tuesday. That is, within a very short space of time, an afternoon, he had a thrombosis in an aorta. Marcus, finding him when he came home, took him to the vet who shook his head and gave him the injection, the dignified route to the end of a very happy, well-fed, healthy and much-loved life. Would that we could all wish the same.*
>
> *Marcus brought him home to High Fold, wrapped up in a towel. I just could not get there in time to say a proper goodbye. Not for him the public cremation, amongst other loved but forsaken bodies, not the ridiculous private affair, where the ashes are kept ever after on the mantlepiece. No, Marcus brought him home, and when I got there, Marcus gave him to me.*
>
> *I dug a hole, amongst the budding daffodils, among the soon-to-be-bursting-forth bluebells, in the place in the garden, where he always sheltered from*

heat or rain. I took him in my arms, placed him gently down, within sound of the sea, his head on his paws, not an hour yet dead and still gently warm, then I crumbled the soil over him. I could not have planted a flower more carefully. Then I took the stones I have collected from myriad beaches near us during our walks together, places he has run over and over, played in the waves, in a life that began in the village and spent rarely more than a few hundred yards from home, other than occasional but traumatic visits to the vet, and placed them over the top of the earth.

Who will welcome me home now, break my ribs in his hello, chew my socks, wag me off at the end of the weekend? There are no words that can contain the sense of loss.

And the next time I saw him, Gerald was sporting a black tie. On anyone else this might have looked ridiculous, a black tie for a dog, but for Gerald, Max was more than a dog. Gerald opened the flat door and put down his bag. There are those who think that there is no more to an affair than sex. For some, presumably, that is true. That day Gerald had not come for sex, coupling in his parlance. Gerald had come for comfort, solace, those things you seek when you grieve. Nothing was said, but I ran across the room and took him in my arms. Tears are more telling than any words. Grieving is often a private emotion but all the more searing for that. And Gerald cried.

Then there was Gerald's tact. There were birthdays (Gerald's was in May), and Christmases and our 'anniversary' of meeting to mark. It is difficult to give someone something that you treasure and hope they will, if they are married. How could Gerald hide whatever my gift was? Gerald could give me the world, and he was exceedingly generous, as I have said, but what could I give him? The man who has everything, or appears to. Mrs W-D was sharing High Fold with him; she had brought that to their marriage, rather like a dowry for the duration of their relationship. Think not upon that, it was beyond our relationship, somewhere else, another planet Gerald occupied when not with me. What could I give him? There was the ubiquitous black-inked pen, Mont Blanc. I gave him one of those, an identical one to the one he had, so that he had one at High Fold (hopefully mine, to remind him of me, silly optimistic, unrealistic me), and one at the office or in his pocket.

I went to that large department store in West London for the pen. I have often thought that the staff in such a place are rather like the last decadent days of a court before the revolution, bored, overpainted, overscented overlabelled, underworked, gossipy, self-indulgent, self-absorbed. Of course I got the only gay and gorgeously camp bloke in the pen section. "Ooohhh, madam," he minced *à la* Frankie Howerd, when I asked for a Mont Blanc. "We'd all like one of those." He laid several out on a cloth. He made various outrageous comments about the length of pens and nibs. My mother would say that particular department store was never like this in the old days. When I came to pay, "Ooohhh, madam," he cooed, "you've been such a good sport, I'll let you use my very special pen." Out came the pen. "*Sooooo* seventies, madam, *sooooo* retro," he prinned. It was a pen with a click. There was a picture of a man on the shaft of the pen. When you clicked the pen, his black pants, which were rather small to start with, disappeared. Off went the sales assistant in gales of laughter. I suggested, rather helpfully I thought, that he write to Father Christmas (it was approaching that time of year) using the pen, with a list of the things he wanted, which would involve a lot of clicking of the pen. "Ooooooohhhh madam is such a wit," he gushed. "So wise, such a sport." I came away a bit stunned. Thankfully, Gerald liked the pen. I did not have to take it back to change it.

Then, of course, there were socks. What is it about a man and his socks? Gerald adored new socks, the freshness, the ironed-ness of them, the still sponginess of them. "Day One, new socks," he could cry, as if something exciting was happening, something life-changing, as he put them on. Sometimes he would pose in them and little else for me. "Look, Sweet, look, my lovely socks!" before collapsing in giggles at his own ridiculousness. Admittedly, they were always the same kind and the same colour, to avoid detection, if the sharp-eyed were checking (though I doubt Mrs W-D did the washing, presumably one of the helpers did this at High Fold), but over the years I bought him masses of socks. He would wear them, all wool ones, or in the summer, cotton or silk, maybe twice or three times at most, revelling in their newness and then discard them (like his women, might I ever so cynically now add here). So socks were always received joyfully. How strange but how useful. Gerald would sometimes say: "You can tell a man's age by how he receives socks. At a certain age, he receives them, but at a later age, he is pleased to receive them."

Otherwise, we would discuss what I could buy sometimes, but once or twice I managed to contrive a surprise, like a painting for his office, behind the brass-polished sign on the door of Wendon-Davis Associates.

I bought it at auction, after Gerald had hinted that he liked a particular artist, who had apparently lived and painted near Great Yarmouth. I haunted auction houses – Sotheby's, Christie's, Bonhams – seeking sales of East Anglian artists, that specific artist. Eventually one came up, one October day, in Bury St Edmunds, deep in the heart of Suffolk. Until that time, I had never participated in an auction, hardly knew what to do. When I saw it, the painting itself took my breath away. Had I truly become so taken over by Gerald, that I would admire his taste in art also? Or is that part of being together, you admire and so share each other's taste? It is a large oil painting of a small boat in the middle of quite a heavy sea and two men in oilskins are toiling, riding the swell of the waves, pulling lobster pots out of the water. There is another boat on the horizon, which in this rolling sea is not far off, and a storm raging overhead. You can almost hear the water lapping below the gunwale. Gerald cited the artist among one of his favourites, *of whom* Gerald wrote in a letter to me, *a critic remarked of his work that his water was wet and his boats floated in the sea.* After what happened, later, I don't know what happened to it, but many times, I saw it in Gerald's office and I know he was much taken with it.

So at the auction, in ancient, much-loved, if rather damp meeting rooms in the Athenaeum near the Cathedral, in Bury – so similar to the mouldering, musty church hall of my childhood – that morning, I settled down at the back of the room. It was a sunny day, still surprisingly warm for so late in the year, the flowers in the cathedral gardens still brilliant, if just beginning their autumn pall. There was an earthy nutty smell in the wind, from the sugar beet factory just on the northern edge of the town – I had seen it from the motorway when I drove in. The annual 'cooking' process, whatever they do to the beets, had clearly begun in earnest. A huge plume of steam signified the culinary arts at work from afar.

Surprisingly we all sat on chairs that were going to be auctioned after the painting sale, incredibly uncomfortable chairs; indeed, several people around me had to keep moving, seeking comfort without success. There were a cluster of dealers along the side wall, all muttering to each other in welcome: "Hah! There must be something significant if you're here!" And in reply, the sardonic: "Why can't you stay in London?" Then much chuckling as they settled down, as if something very funny had been said, making room for each other against the furniture. Thus lined up, mustered and prepared, we were under starter's orders, and then off! The auction began.

My painting was number 375 in the catalogue. The selling went on, the auctioneer's head like a tennis audience, right, left, the price with me, the price with you, at the back of the room, on the phone, in the middle, at the back. He cajoled us, persuaded, another thousand here, five hundred there. He entreated "Come on, sir," when someone dallied over a price, banged his head with the hammer in frustration, prices went up, some did not make a sale. "Well done, madam, thank you," as someone raised their hand; people muttered into phones and nodded, his hammer punctuated the proceedings, making the bargain. Down the sale booklet we went. Many of the pictures were enough to make one shake one's head at in wonderment – who on earth would pay £4,000 for that, but then on this occasion I knew, I could see, the woman or the man was sitting across the room from me. Or £500 for that, but they did. Then suddenly it was 373, my heart thumping, 374, where does the time go? Thump, thump, then Lot 375.

Now I had made friends with one of the ladies from the auction house during the viewing the day before and she recognised me as I came in this day. "Don't bid straight away," she advised. "If no one bids, the price may drop." So I paused. There was the starter price, which to my surprise was considerably less than the lower price indicated in the catalogue. Someone took it. Up went my hand, with my register number in it. The auctioneer did not see it! I was too far back – the painting might go! I waved the number around, all nerves, heat and desperation. The picture, I must have the picture. Gerald would love it so much. I waved and waved the paper. Did I make a fool of myself again? Was there time to care? The auctioneer turned, he saw! He named my price. I nodded, my heart pounding, tongue tied. "With you, madam, at the back of the room." The other party played with that price. To me, the auctioneer: "Another £500, madam?" My ticket went up again. God this was nerve-racking stuff. Yes? Yes? Going… "Sold! To the back of the room," sang the auctioneer, completing the deal and already leaning forward for my number. 'Wham' went the hammer. Just like the 'dong' on old-fashioned cash tills.

Yes, to me. Really. My first painting bought at auction. I knew Gerald was perfectly *au fait* with this world and this process – he was always talking about pictures bought here, sold there – but it was my first. So exciting! I was shaking like a leaf. How can people do this for a living? But so exhilarating. And what a painting, a very large painting. I managed – with some difficulty and with the help of my new-found friend – to get it in the back of the car and I hugged myself all the way back to London with the very anticipated pleasure of Gerald's reaction when he saw what I had achieved.

And he did not let me down. "Sweeting, Sweeting, my Princess, my pearl beyond price, what have you done?" he crowed when he saw it, holding it at arm's length, all aflame with delight. It was worth everything I paid for it and more. In that moment, I would have gone through fire for him, just to have that look of delight in his eyes. "What a wonderful picture, you clever Sweeting; my lovely, how did you do it?" Crediting me as if he had had no part in selecting it. If I could have bought him a thousand such pictures I would have, just for that moment of his unadulterated, utter happiness. In a lifetime, it is difficult to find presents for people they really want and appreciate, but Gerald that day, he was on top of the world with pleasure.

Another day – one cold December day in 1990 – Gerald took me with him on a pheasant shoot. It was a risky thing to do so publicly, sometimes madly typical of Gerald's intermittent discretion. In a relationship such as ours was, it would be rare to be seen together in public, or rather, to be seen at the same function as a couple. The gossip magazines and columns would have had a field day, had we been 'discovered' together. However, it appeared I should not have worried. It was clearly too far from London, too cold or too close to Christmas for the photographers and journalists who might otherwise have spoilt the day. Perhaps Gerald already knew that. Indeed, it was a very grey and dank sort of day, with hardly any wind. "A good day for shooting," remarked Gerald, in a lordly sort of way.

When we arrived at the farm, there were several H&Hs of Gerald's whom I knew from the City. Certainly I was greeted warmly and without any side glances or snide remarks. It was accepted that I was a guest of Gerald's and that was enough. No one asked any more questions. There was much talk amongst some of the men there about Mrs Thatcher's leaving office and the international atmosphere that was heating up, just prior to the first Gulf War. The inspectors were not having much success in Iraq and troop numbers and equipment were building in the Gulf area. Someone said: "This John Major, he's a bit grey and prissy for my taste," and Gerald responded, "Well anyone would be after Maggie," and everyone laughed as though it was funny. Gerald had remained a fan of Mrs Thatcher's, even throughout the excesses of some of her latter years. In this, his faithfulness was remarkable given his proclivities in other now well-documented areas. On John Major, well it was early days yet, at that point; Gerald as jury was still out. This was years before the revelations about his private life at that time, long before the jokes about a Major-Currie relationship. Looking back at that time – well, looking at all of this – you realise afresh the power of twenty-twenty vision. How blinded with innocence, even then, after eight years with Gerald, I was.

The air was chilled and bracing, and Gerald fussed about the car, urging me to put extra layers on, more socks, paying my subscription into the sweepstake into guessing the number of birds to be shot, making sure I would be warm and dry. It was terribly sweet, a whole side of Gerald I had never seen before – and Gerald in a country pursuit, that was new. His friends all came up, either to introduce themselves or to say hello to us both and ask how we both were. Gerald was clearly well known and respected. There was no mention of Mrs W-D, who had been in the headlines that week, as spokesperson for something connected with the troop build-up. Rather there were comments of "Lovely day for it," as people surveyed the sky or "Where are we starting?" and finally, "Gather round, gentlemen, oh and young lady," and there was a sort of titter at that, as we gathered around for instructions.

We were all loaded into a gun cart with the shoot dogs, beautiful sleek black retrievers in our midst. Gerald had borrowed someone else's for the day. The dog and I, recognising our statuses, took to each other. He was borrowed, I was a borrower. I borrowed Gerald. I learned the dog's name was Thor. He dribbled over me a little as we rumbled along in the cart, with all the others, resting his beautiful head on my knee. In the cramped gun cart, I was crushed between Gerald and one of his City friends. There was warmth in the masses of bodies, both of men and animals. And me with my borrowed man, borrowed dog.

Even now, years after the event, I can remember there is such a stillness and a silence about the shoot. We tramped over the winter wheat from beat to beat, getting mud-weighted boots. The wind was so cold, my teeth ached. We all lined up on what I learned were our pegs, which to me looked like the points on a clock around a central point. Then silently we waited for the beaters to creep around the fields and up through the undergrowth of sweetcorn remains, then position themselves to drive the birds towards the guns. And… in the waiting, time hangs… the silence deepens… you listen to the wind, the occasional train in the distance, the rumble of a car across a far field, horses nearby, the dogs whining slightly with anticipation. And in the humans, each mind stills… thoughts begin to fade… such is the concentration, the watching, the silence… breath itself almost stills. And you wait.

Then seeing the birds, a very explosion of indignant feathered shock, the guns raised without thought, spot your bird, stay with it, the 'bang', which is much louder than expected, a ringing in your ears, the shot splaying in the air behind the bird, the bellow of the gun echoing off the trees in the wood, then spinning round to see where the bird has gone, have you got it, is it falling, is it still hovering on the wind current, has it fallen, is it running, shall I set the dog after it? A thousand questions, repeated over and over, as all about there are songbirds and hares crashing out of the hedges and woods, to the reverberation of the guns, before the gentle rain of unused shot returning to earth.

Where a bird floundered, fell in a huge fuss of feathers but somehow otherwise would then pick themselves up and otherwise run, I quickly learned to release Thor. True as an arrow, he raced to each bird, or as Gerald would say, proudly marvelling: "Just look at that animal go, straight as a gun barrel." Back Thor would come, tail wagging, the bird secure in his soft mouth, jubilant that he had performed well. "Oh, well played," Gerald would say after each beat and shooting had finished, breaking the gun open sometimes or just taking the gun slip back from me to cover the gun, putting out his hand to me to take Thor's lead. "All right, my lovely?" he would enquire. I tramped along beside Gerald as happy as I could ever be. We became muddier. With some distaste, I took a dead partridge from Thor's soft jaws, the tiny bird all crumpled where it had fluttered, for the last time, down to earth. I found, to my surprise, a quiet pleasure in the soft plumage of its neck feathers and a gentle but dying heat against the palm of my hand. Thor thumped his tail approvingly. We were both pleased with ourselves.

My heart sang, with the pleasure of the day, the cold air, being warm inside, and Gerald's company, his laughter, his jokes. Gerald was aflame with the pleasure of being out in the fresh air, no phones, no pressure, just being outside, doing something he loved. He helped me down, along and up ditches, through hedges, round waterlogged ground. "Come on, my lovely, let's be having you," he would wink at me as he handed me over a stile. Several times I would look up from attending to Thor, to see Gerald looking over his shoulder for me, his face all concern until he saw me smile. "All well?" he'd whisper. Then such a smile came back before he turned to the gun again.

For some reason that day, the jokes improved slightly. To my taking and holding things he said: "This is like being on safari." To which I muttered back: "Yes and all we need now is a lion and a bit of sun." Later he said: "I feel like a memsahib." To which I responded: "I think you will find I'm the memsahib. I may know little about shooting but I know my memsahibs from my sahibs!" We grinned and then looked at each other askance, for of course I was not married, not legally anyway. Only in my heart.

Sometimes the dog was not as obedient as he should have been. At one point we were trying to check a ditch for birds. On this occasion, Thor would not co-operate. "Find it, find it," urged Gerald. Thor would have none of it. With a sparkle in his eye and a waggle in his tail, he looked very pleased with himself but he would not get in the ditch. In the end, Gerald slid down the slope and with a deadpan delivery said: "Why have a dog when you can bark yourself?" as he stood in the ditch bottom. Of course I laughed, who wouldn't have done? Gerald loved it when I laughed at his jokes. All men do. Cynical me. Cynical now, but not then. Then I just worshipped the ground he walked on. Or in this instance, the ditch he stood in.

We had lunch in an old barn, on an assortment of old chairs (as I was the only woman they found me a pink chair and cleaned it off, making such a gallant fuss), packed lunches out of boxes and bags amid the tractors, the wood shavings, and general farm equipment. As it was close to Christmas, someone produced mince pies, hot sausage rolls all washed down with port, which warmed you down to your toes. They all fussed round me, anxious that I should enjoy it all. Despite all that happened to me through Gerald, this day stands out as a beacon of such kindness, such happiness.

After lunch, we resumed our places, surrounding another desiccated patch of maize, waiting for the beaters, waiting for the birds. This time, we were on the slope of a hill, leading down to a ditch before the land rose again up to the farm we had lunched at. As the first shots began slowly to ring out – the birds were obviously reluctant to move – my eye was caught suddenly by a small child emerging at the side of the hedge, standing on a small bridge, in front of the guns. In front of the guns. What chilling words. A cold hand wraps itself around my heart even now at the memory. At times like these, life seems to go into slow motion as the image sears itself into your memory. Not what does happen but what could happen. The nearest hunter stopped, like me, with his heart in his mouth and even at the distance I was standing from him, I could envisage the urgency in his mind and voice as he urged the child to come to him. Without words, the other men waited, distracted – thank God – from their task. In the ceasefire, the child ran obediently to his father's side and everyone breathed again, returning to their murderous sport.

Later we gathered round whilst the beaters and the dogs retrieved the birds from stubble or ditch or ploughed field. The child came to the group with his father and one of the older boys, wearing a flat cap and thinking himself mature, who had beaten but was not collecting birds, asked him his name.

We all looked at him then. And from under the most delicately curled eyelashes, against a peachy skin, still redolent of warm summer days, the child looked up with huge brown eyes and said: "Giles." Asked what he had been doing, he looked first to his father, with a flicker of those eyelashes, and replied smiling, without any hesitation, "Playing football," and with a huge rush of pleasure, "and we won!" His father smiled at the boy and so did Gerald. We all smiled, the boy was so enchanting. The moment hung in the air briefly whilst we all enjoyed the boy's pure pleasure in his morning's outcome before some of the group began to move on. I would have moved too, but not before I had seen Gerald give such a piercing look of envy, at the man and his son. There are some things that money and success cannot bring you. Gerald handed the boy a boiled sweet, and the boy, seeking a nod from his father, took it. Not the bag, this was men amongst men. Such courtesies would be fussed over by women. Giles sighed happily, elevated to a status he would never attain at his age amongst women. Gerald was smiling then as he turned away, such a wistful smile. What Gerald would have given to have had a son, to be the other half of that inner circle, man and boy, sharing the same blood, quietly adoring each other.

We finished in the half-light of that late December afternoon, as the sky was beginning to clear to the east and the frost was beginning to fall with the dust. I remember that wonderful exhaustion. We trampled through the crisping fields, where the frost was hardening. Tired, chilled, the wind stinging our faces, covered in mud, we were rocked in the back of the cart over the ruts of frost on the road to the farm as the beaters tied the birds into braces. Such birds! There they lay, to be counted and then picked up by the shooters and then the beaters, to be carried away as prizes of the day, to be hung, dressed and then eventually casseroled. By then, in the twilight cold of midwinter, they were so beautiful against the grey concrete underfoot. Such a richness of plumage, fit for a king's coat. Forever afterwards, whenever I see those tiny partridges or the magnificent pheasants hanging high up on the market stalls, around the still-cobbled streets of Leadenhall Market, with fancy prices against them, I am reminded of that chill afternoon and the tingling exhaustion over my body, after a day in the air with Gerald. And Thor. A borrowed man and a borrowed dog.

The moon was high in the night sky even at four thirty that winter afternoon. A high and searing brilliance in the night sky, it was shining on the road, like a silver river as Gerald drove us to yet another of his various friends' cottages. "Hard to believe," commented Gerald as we bumped up the unmade drive in his latest Jaguar, totally unsuitable for the terrain, "that in the height of summer we'd still have another five and a half hours or so of daylight left." In the bright moonlight, Gerald managed to get the key in the door first go. The door was a bit stiff with the damp.

How very convenient these love nests were. Refreshed with brandies, we sank into hot steaming baths, groaning at the pain of cold skin set aglow by hot water, risking chilblains. I can hear my mother warning me against such things. But who worries about chilblains when you are in love? And after such a day! Whilst I had my bath, the brandy warming my stomach, Gerald built up the fire till the whole cottage was warm. Over dinner, much of which Gerald produced from a hamper, he pretended to be that Frenchman from the Cointreau adverts in the seventies, where "The warmth of we French eez combined with zee frost of you Englishee." He had an appalling accent. Of course I laughed; he was very funny that night, flushed, full of sparkle at his shooting successes and a day in the air. Too tired even to make love, later we fell asleep in front of the glowing embers, in a big exhausted heap on the sofa bed in the sitting room.

Later that night, about 3am, when it was very cold, I arose to go to the bathroom. As I came back, picking my way across the darkened room, using the moonlight as a guide, Gerald muttered in the darkness: "My Diane, my lovely Diane." I froze. Diane is not my given name. Was he talking in his sleep? Who was she? Gerald chuckled, a warm, rosy sound in the dark. He was awake: "You, you fool, you great pudding, my Diane, goddess of hunting." He pulled me back into the warmth of the bed. "Did you think I was dreaming about another woman when I have got you?" as he enveloped me in his arms, the heat of his body defrosting mine. "What a silly girl you are," as we cuddled up against each other, snuggling back into the covers. It was of course an easy mistake to make. I did not stop then as I might have done later and added to Gerald's sentence *when I have got you here.* He loved whom he was with at the time. My heart had been broken for less. I did not dwell on that, for this night, on the verge of sleep, cuddling up very close, imagine my pleasure when he whispered in my ear: "I was so proud of you today, Sweeting." Imitating what he thought passed for a Tarzan voice, he murmured: "Girl done well." Even now, long after, awakened utterly from Sleeping Beauty's hundred-year sleep, I can still see his sleepy smile when I shut my eyes.

Would that it had always been like that, the light in his eyes reserved only for me, the smile, the joy, all for me, all mine. I lived for such moments, as fleeting, unexpected and rare as they were. And ask yourself, as I so frequently did: if that was enough for me, why not him? Indeed, ask yourself this: if it was enough for Mrs W-D and I, wasn't that enough for him? But no, sadly, heartbreakingly, apparently no.

12

The Night Before, the Morning After

Then there was the small matter of the *ménage a trois*. I recall it was around Gerald's birthday, one of the special ones, when I received a call from him. Gerald's birthday was in May, and this one was in 1997, not long after the election of New Labour to power. Gerald must have been forty-eight by then. He was not best pleased by the outcome of the election but not that surprised. I don't think anyone was by that time. Mrs W-D had retained her seat, but then it was a safe one and her majority was considerably reduced, but that is another story, not for these pages.

"Come over, Sweeting," he boomed down the phone one evening, "Come over. I have a proposition to put to you." With no other detail I went. See how obedient I was in those days.

When I got to the flat, the inner door was open and, as I went in, I could hear voices. I got to the sitting area, as Gerald liked to call it, with the huge backdrop of the western sky and the setting sun. There was Gerald, opening what looked like a second bottle of champagne and a girl, standing with her back to me, watching the sky. Gerald effected the introductions. She had a very firm handshake. For Gerald's predilections, she was rather, well, rather boy-like, very slim, a waif, I suppose he would describe her. She was terribly pretty though, which was certainly to Gerald's taste. I was still none the wiser as to the proposition, till he came to us both with fresh glasses and said: "Welcome to my fantasy." And then I knew. The three of us, for his birthday present. I looked at her dumbfounded. She smiled back. The idea of the three of us did not seem to bother her. I registered in a remote part of my brain that her teeth were not that good. (I wonder now what it is about Gerald and what I can only call his harem that I always think of racehorses.)

I turned to Gerald and, in the same movement, gave him back the glass. He looked slightly startled at the gesture but in that same moment he knew. "Sweeting," he pleaded, "it's just for one night, just to see." And finally, "It is my birthday," as if that would excuse any behaviour, however abhorrent I might find it.

"No, Gerald," said I more firmly than I knew I could. "Never. I want no part of this. Goodnight." I was sickened by the whole thing. He moved his face then to that mule-ish expression he adopted when he wanted something he could not have. After all, it is not in the role of a mistress to decline. Perhaps it is in the role of a wife to have the privilege of denial, to refuse. Was I just a plaything, without feelings, to be toyed with and then put back in the box? No. I was in love with him but I would not participate in one of his sexual games. Why could I not be enough? He was everything to me, everything. Could this be the same man who had looked after me, worried for me on the day of the shoot? It was impossible! He was impossible!

I moved towards my coat, shaking with anger, embarrassment; the indignity of it all. This was one of the few times in our relationship I rebelled. Good, eh? Gerald did look surprised. Fancy, my Sweeting is not so obedient after all. Perhaps Sleeping Beauty turned in her hundred-year sleep at that point.

Funnily enough, before I turned to go, I turned to the girl: Sandy was her name, I remember now, and we bowed slightly, rather as those Japanese sumo wrestlers do before and after combat. We shook hands very formally. I noticed she had rather larger hands than one might have expected, with beautifully manicured nails. I saw that she smiled as I gathered my things from where I had just put them. I let myself out.

I realised when I had got home again that I had left a book there by accident that I needed the next day but thought no more of it that night. I was too hurt and offended to go back. And who knew what might be happening. I even turned Gerald's photograph to the wall before I went to bed. Pathetic I know, but I felt at the time it was a meaningful gesture. Of course, I slept badly. Was something unpleasant abroad in the air that night? My imagination worked overtime.

The next morning, I duly returned. The front door at the base of the tower block was locked as it should be, but I had a key. I let myself in and went up. Funnily enough once again, as I got to Gerald's flat, the inner door was open, though it should not have been as he would have been at the office by then, haranguing poor Wendy, doubtless. Or so I thought. I opened the door fully and went in.

"Hello?" came a quivery voice "Who's there?" It was Gerald, still there. Was something wrong? Was he ill? I pushed opened the bedroom door and there he was. Almost naked, other than a pair of socks (usually the first things to come off in such circumstances, I distantly reminded myself). He was spread-eagled across the bed, handcuffed to the bed head, looking, in Gerald-ese, as utterly discombobulated as I have ever seen him. What a good word, discombobulated. It really suited him on this occasion. I began to say, 'What happened to you?' but it seemed all too self-evident. But the handcuffs?

There was more. To my amusement, any physical sign of which was instantly removed from my face, someone, presumably Sandy of the night before, had written on his tummy in black-tip pen, *I woz 'ere*, with a large arrow pointing down towards Gerald's groin. Gerald looked completely ridiculous, rather like a parcel with a huge address across his middle. All he needed was a stamp. And posting. I could not laugh – one did not laugh at Gerald. Or not in front of him at such a time.

"Oh, Sweeting, thank God it is you," cried Gerald, looking a thousand years older than I have seen him at that time in the morning. "Thank the Lord it is you. I have been so worried Mrs Oliver might come in. It's her morning." Mrs Oliver. I clapped my hand to my forehead. Of course. It had to be that morning. Of all days. In my shock at the scene in front of me I had not given her a thought. She was another of Gerald's army of doers; this time she was the cleaning lady. At the best of times, she had a sour expression, clearly taking a dim view of some of Gerald's highly questionable goings-on. Rightly so perhaps, as I was apparently discovering. A scene I have witnessed half a dozen times came to mind.

"Mrs Oliver..." Gerald, in happier times fancying himself a thespian, striking what he called his Dickensian pose, would pose thoughtfully, head back, hands on his lapels, clearly about to say something profound, "...has a face..." deep breath, for dramatic impression, observation lofty, looking down the whole length of his nose, "...like a bulldog licking piss off a thistle. She is, if I may be so bold," looking at me with screwed-up eyes, "as cold as a witch's tit." Pause for more breath, pushing out the chest: "Imagine, my dear," he would say expansively, "imagine what Mr Oliver must have done in a previous life, to wake up next to that!" So saying, Gerald would wink at me, from the height of his pomposity and then collapse with laughter, making me giggle with him. Gerald modelled himself, fancied himself, as a latter-day Laurence Olivier. Disregard the lack of talent, the chins, the expanding waistband and a tendency on Gerald's part to only act in a pompous fashion, the second Olivier he liked to believe he could be. We would giggle together at such times; it did sound truly shocking from him, most un-Gerald-like; were these all Norfolk phrases? Did he pick them up at High Fold? Most unlikely I should have thought. Perhaps there was an alternative life in the constituency. Back to reality, back to that morning, just imagine how she would take this particular scene in.

Well, of course, I rushed to find her number, stumbling around the room, over the debris of the night before. There seemed rather a lot of bottles. I rang her, managed to catch her before she got her bus and headed her off. "Yes," I said into the phone. "Come this afternoon, Mrs Oliver, that would be most helpful. Gerald is... er, working in the flat this morning." Funny though, even now when I remember this whole incident, I think of Mrs Oliver and her peppermints. She was a heavy smoker of cheap cigarettes and somehow the illusion from her school days – many of them doubtless spent behind the bicycle sheds – that peppermint overwhelmed the smell of smoke had stayed with her. Whenever she was nearby or had been in the flat, there was always the faint whiff of the combination of scents, that she so faithfully adhered to. God knows what her teeth and lungs were like. The peppermints, however, did nothing for her facial expression. In happier times, Gerald had even suggested, "Perhaps she is walking evidence of what happens when the wind changes," before reaching happily to tickle me.

That extraordinary morning, fortunately she had agreed, albeit with her usual bad grace, not to come till later in the day. I was effusive in my thanks, fumbling with the words as Gerald nodded at me, prostrate as he was from the bed. Best to keep this matter to as few people as possible. Imagine, as was always the case with Gerald, the headlines. *MP's husband found handcuffed to bed after night of torrid passion* etc. It hardly bore thinking about. The gossip pages would have had a field day. Then I tried to search for the key to the cuffs but, presumably, Sandy had taken it with her. Gerald saw what I was doing and said, rather sheepishly: "It was thrown out of the window." It seemed pointless to ask for more details. In the end, rather than call for the fire brigade – at the suggestion of which Gerald shuddered, as far as you can when you are handcuffed to the bed – I rang Marcus, faithful, still then, highly scented Marcus.

It was his day off. When he came to the phone, it was obvious I had just wakened him. "Marcus," I began briskly enough. "It's me. I'm at Gerald's. Can you come over? Now?"

Marcus began to acquiesce. "Oh, and Marcus, can you bring some good wire cutters?" Marcus began to chuckle. I did not explain but it was obvious he had worked out some part of what had happened. It was then I began to relax a bit and truly see the funny side. Gerald would have been appalled if he had heard us. The indignity of it. "Heavy-duty cutters," I managed to say in between giggles.

"I shall be there shortly," promised the ever-reliable Marcus.

While we waited for Marcus, I sat on the bed, to keep Gerald company. The bedside clock ticked electronically away, flashing as it changed the minutes. Companionably, we had a cup of tea together, except that I held Gerald's cup whilst he sipped. It was almost like feeding someone who was ill or hurt in some way, blowing on the tea for him to cool it a bit, tipping the cup up, watching over the rim to see if he had neared the liquid, tipping it a bit more, then he would raise his hands to indicate he had had sufficient. At first, we hardly mentioned the strangeness of it all as we sat there. I think he was just relieved I was there, the end to his seemingly awful night was nearing. But I did wonder. The handcuffs – I had never known about Gerald and handcuffs, this was a mystery – had chaffed his wrists and I wondered how he would explain the marks away to Mrs W-D. Could he wear sweatbands for a day or so? And in bed with her? But it was not my place to ask. And remarkably really, I didn't even allude to them. But as we sat together, I did my best to rub off the ink, making a black smudge across his tummy. It did not look good. His tummy became very red where I had rubbed it.

Finally we had finished the tea. This seemed to stir Gerald into conversation. "Sweet, it was awful, just awful," he bemoaned his fate, seeking my sympathy. "What a night! I must be losing my touch. Or my sight." I looked at him askance. "Oh, I know she looked like a bird," (Gerald was a child of the sixties) "and I met her as a girl at a show. Well she looked like a girl." He tried hard to look contrite, to make me feel sorry for him. "But last night, Sweeting," and here he shuddered dramatically again, which was still a fairly limited gesture, "we got into bed; all was going well and I put my hand down there, you know, old girl, to warm the old starter motor." Here I did look at him hard. What kind of a conversation was this to have with your mistress? "Blow me," he went on as if nothing had happened, "no pun intended," he said hastily, as I looked at him again even harder, "she had a handle! She was a bloke!"

We digested this quietly, each alone with our thoughts. It is strange to hear your lover describe a night with someone else, especially if the someone else is not all they appear to be. I began to think I was receiving too much information. Self-disgust was beginning to overwhelm me. Just think, in a more ridiculous frame of mind last night I might have stayed. What might have happened? But Gerald had not finished his musing. "Well, I was out of that bed before you could say 'showgirl'. Fancy being in bed with another bloke." He paused for dramatic effect, drew himself up – as much as he could in his present position. "I, Gerald Wendon-Davis, pulled a bloke. What is the world coming to?" We were silent again, reflecting on that.

Gerald cleared his throat. Clearly at this stage I was not looking sufficiently sorry for him. Gerald began to look more doleful. He tried again. "I feel..." deep breath, more effect. "Sweeting, I feel defiled," he finished lamely over the last word, finally realising what he had asked me to do last night, when Sandy's sex was less apparent. There was no apology though. I suppose now, well, I can admit it now since everything else is out in the open – I was taken for granted, part of the wallpaper of his life. I was a habit, one he no longer actually recognised as anything else. Naturally it did not occur to him on this occasion to apologise.

How had Gerald ended up handcuffed? "Oh," said Gerald disarmingly, as indeed at that moment he was, "Sandy thought she, I mean, he, would show me a stunt." I stared at him and he looked away. It was difficult sometimes to take him seriously. There was worse to come. It was at that moment rather absentmindedly I thought to pick up one of the spare pillows that had fallen to the floor. I gasped, pulling back, thinking from first glance it was a snake. In fact, it was a whip. A very long, black leather whip. And beside that, an opened packet of condoms. And a tube of K-Y Jelly, with a big squeeze in the middle of it, like the toothpaste in happier times Gerald and I squabbled over – like a married couple (Gerald, ever tidy, precise Gerald squeezed from the end, I from the middle. Presumably Sandy had also squeezed in the middle, or Gerald, in passionate haste...?). How far away that world seemed now. Make no mistake; I am just an ordinary girl, born to normal parents, in an ordinary village who happened to grow up to be someone's mistress. This was new territory to me.

When people say their jaw dropped, now I know what that feels like. Mine seemed to dislocate. My eyes rose to meet Gerald's. It was preposterous to ask whose it all was. "Sandy's calling card," he muttered, dropping his eyes away from mine. A veil began to clear from my sight. It was all lies. He had known how I would react to his original suggestion, had in his tangled and convoluted way driven me out, to somehow make his forthcoming actions permissible. Is that what it was about? Was this the lowest point in our relationship? No, no, remarkably as I can see it now, we still had depths to plumb or to plummet into before that point. But the truth, on this particular morning, I was not now anxious to hear.

Gerald has often said bitterness does not suit me. In moments of terrible temper, amongst other things, I have called him a satyr, which oddly enough is a term he always found deeply offensive. Other times I have called him a sybarite. It is not normally a term of abuse, of course, but there was no point in swearing at Gerald – he became very snooty and you only ended up feeling foolish. And ranting never did any good. This time, there was nothing else left. "What's the *pièce de résistance*, Gerald, the remains of a line of white power or a used hypodermic needle?" I spat out at him. "Just how far will you push yourself, to seek the next pleasure?" He looked away completely then. "And just how much do you intend to humiliate and debase those around you?" He did not answer. There was a terrible quiet.

Just then Marcus arrived. To save Gerald's dignity – that is, what he had left of it – I had covered him over with the sheet and put the whip into a cupboard. The condoms went into the bin, to be retrieved later and disposed of before Mrs Oliver found them. The less she had to think over, in that flat, the better. I never found the used one, if indeed there was one. I would like to think that there wasn't but then I like to delude myself. Looking back, I sometimes ask myself why I didn't leave Gerald then but I know the answer. And that morning, when Marcus arrived, the question had already gone from my thoughts, its arrival unnoted; if such is possible, the question unasked. Somehow, the sight of Marcus – normal, ordinary, wonderful, heroic Marcus – turned the world back to normal, steadied it on its axis. The familiar assuages the fear. We all just got on with getting on. I was in love with Gerald. That Gerald, of the previous night, disappeared with Marcus coming in through the door.

It turned out that Marcus was a former fireman as well as being part of what I now consider the Brighton mafia, but was otherwise known as Gerald's army of hairdressers, manicurists, chauffeurs and who knew what else. As professional as you would expect from such a pedigree, Marcus kept his face straight before his employer, whom Lord knows looked completely ridiculous, apparently almost naked but for the socks and the sheet, handcuffed and with a long black smudge on his stomach. Unspoken, it was just assumed that Gerald had had a wild night with an unknown woman. Neither Gerald nor I cared set the record straight. But Marcus made no comment, setting to with a very professional-looking set of metal cutters and within minutes Gerald was released. Thank goodness it was not Mr Fred (*of whom privately I think of as SD, or Sperm Donor*, Gerald had written in a particularly acerbic letter I have kept), whom at the time Gerald had just succeeded in silencing by injunction for the second time before he tried again to spill the beans on his former employer. Mr Fred haunted Gerald. And made many lawyers rich before he had finished.

Marcus helped Gerald off to the shower as, having lain in such a difficult position for so long, Gerald was a bit stiff. It was not difficult to work out what might have happened. This was the view I could live with at that point. See how well I could live in a state of delusion, when the truth could be too unpalatable to think upon. My version of the night that I could live with was that Gerald was unfit, for all his bravado and sexual antics, which was true. After whatever had happened, happened, the Sandy person, of indeterminate sexual inclination, had overcome him, tied him to the bedpost, robbed him of the cash in his wallet and left the front door ajar, so that Gerald would be rescued in due course. The trick with the door was a kind of sop so that Sandy would not presumably be accused of murder. There were other alternatives hinted at, which made Sandy crueller and Gerald more compliant, paying for Sandy's services, but I preferred this view, however much of a work of fiction it all was. I did not care to know what was true and not true.

Thinking back on this now, it was something verging on a miracle that, apart from Mr Fred, no one else talked to the press about Gerald's antics, not even Sandy on this particular occasion. When I think now of the dangers, the risks, the stories, such discretion is remarkable in an age of sprinkling so-called secrets liberally across all the media. We were all discreet for him and it seemed the more we tried to keep things quiet and contained, the worse he got. Gerald would not learn, was not in the mood to learn. The more choice, the more variety, the more spice, the better, whatever the risks. And I? I was learning in a different way, just not fast enough.

There was one thing that came out of this particularly disgusting episode. I never asked Gerald the specifics of that night and as futile as it was for his habits, I made Gerald have an AIDS test. He created an almighty fuss about it but he did it. Neither of us mentioned the press and what happened if they found out he'd had a test. Stranger things have happened, been leaked. Maybe he felt he owed me, by my very silence on the events of that night. To be honest, it wasn't the first test or indeed the last. By then it was the mid-nineties, over the mass panic of the initial onset of the disease and I know you are only as good as the last test, but I felt it was a point of principle. Perhaps very slowly I was learning to protect myself. And him.

13

Greg

And then there was Greg. Well, of course it was self-evident that Greg was more than a nephew. Greg adored Gerald and Gerald adored Greg. That was the overriding emotion. Greg was that son Gerald never had. And down the years, sharing Gerald with Greg, even though of course, Greg was not there, I knew of when Greg's voice broke, how Greg's exams were going, the piano practice, the new bicycle Gerald had bought him, the occasional lunches in London and then a show afterwards, or in Cambridge, closer to Greg's school in the Midlands. I knew when Greg broke his arm at games and how it was mending, and what Gerald had written on the plaster. I knew of his Christmas presents to Gerald and I went with Gerald several times to choose Greg's. Greg was good at cricket and rugby, so it came as something of a surprise that apparently his ambition was to be a dress designer. I wondered what his aunt, Mrs W-D, made of that – an opportunity for more Bright Green Suits – but I knew that he could do no wrong in Gerald's eyes. And presumably the reverse was true. Certainly Gerald worked to make it so.

Then one day, I got a garbled message at work, to "ring someone called Wendy, wouldn't leave her surname. Something about an accident." How thoughtless was this, the message taker? An incomplete message, with terrible possibilities. My heart stopped, the world rocked. As a robot I went to the phone. There was only one Wendy and she was Gerald's right hand. There were some chilling moments as I waited for the connection, waited for someone to get her to come to the phone. Gerald, Gerald, what had happened? Don't die on me. She knew my voice. I said her name, somehow pulling the sound from the depths of my lungs, which were suddenly finding it hard to work.

"Hello," she said, realising immediately that it was me and that I was in shock. "Gerald has called. He's at St Thomas's. It's Greg, he's in the Accident and Emergency there, he's had an accident. He fell off the back of a friend's motorbike."

The world righted, stopped rocking. I sobbed with relief, the first proper intake of air for some minutes. "You poor thing," she sympathised, when I managed to get proper breathing re-established. "What a dreadful thing to do, not to take the message properly. I am so sorry, you must have had a terrible few minutes." Wendy was very kind, very discreet, the perfect PA. And a very nice human being.

Now this does not reflect well on me. But Greg was not my son, my nephew or anything other than a competitor, albeit one amongst many, for Gerald's affection. Indeed, in my more petulant, childish moments, I cursed him for often being the front-runner for Gerald's time and love. Put bluntly, Gerald was loyal to Greg in the way he could never be to a woman. But it was still Gerald I was concerned for. How could I not respond? When I could, I ran home, got a hat, rushed to the hospital. The hat? Remember, I was only the mistress and even in times of disaster, you must still remember your place. Extraordinary now, looking back, that even at such a time, I still thought to be discreet. Without this, gaffes can be made, a cover blown.

Then how to get hold of Gerald? At that time, you could not use a mobile phone in a hospital. I pulled the hat down, so that my face was hidden under the brim. Looking back now, this was bordering on the ridiculous – I probably looked more conspicuous than without it. However, I walked through the corridors, looking and looking, to the A&E unit and there he was, Gerald, even now elegant, but very drawn, the skin very bruised under his eyes, but otherwise very pale. He looked so tired. My heart turned over for him. But I could not run to him, even then. Do not forget yourself in public – I learned that lesson from Ascot. I looked at him hard from under the brim, whilst still moving, and I had the pleasure in that strange and stressed place, amid all those damaged bodies, of seeing his eyes widen in recognition, a smile in them, if not on his lips. But he could not rise and come to me. Turning to his neighbour, he muttered something like, "Just going outside for some air," as he began to get up. Would you believe it, the chap next to him said he'd have some too!

Out they came. What a surprise. There I was, waiting under the canopy, in the night air, the noise of London all around me, waiting to meet my lover, and I got two men of whom, one was the desired man and the other, well, words fail me… the grease-laden, slicked-back hair just revolted me. Is the first rule a mistress learns patience? I had to wait whilst they talked and the other – the unknown and unwanted – man smoked a cigarette.

Then he went in and Gerald was mine, but not mine undivided. Greg had been mashed badly in the accident, he was going through to intensive care. I am not indifferent to the suffering of another human being but Greg's specific injuries are not part of this story. What is, is that night and for several nights thereafter, Gerald came to stay in the flat with me, ostensibly to be nearer to Greg, so he said, but I like to think that he could not bear to be in his own flat alone, he needed the comfort of another human more than ever then. During the first night, when at long last the hospital sent Gerald home, during the small hours when things were still very bad for Greg, I woke to find him pacing round the room.

"Do you think he will make it?" Gerald murmured. "I'd give my life for his." Clearly looking back now, it was a long dark night in the wastelands of Gerald's heart. Perhaps there was more than a spark of humanity in him, a degree of selflessness yet uncharted but perhaps I am letting cynicism, jealousy, overwhelm rational thought. Then of course, I thought nothing of this, I just knew he needed simple human comfort and I called him back to bed, back to the warm. Of course Greg would be all right I said – though I did not know, not then. And he would recover, I was confident for Gerald. I did not countenance the idea of Gerald's life for Greg's; Gerald had already committed enough to the Devil. At such times, it is not sex that is the comfort, it is the warmth and the presence of another person, that carries you through the darkest hours. And I wiped Gerald's tears away, rocked him, soothed him, as far as it was possible when his heart and his mind were somewhere else. And then who could blame him?

After what seemed a considerable time, the enchantment that is the preserve of the young worked and Greg healed. Not totally, not perfectly, even with youth on his side. Gerald would tell me of Greg's headaches and that Greg did not play rugby anymore. For me, it was an interesting discovery. As a mistress, it might be construed that you dream that ultimately you want to marry the man you love. Some women are wives, some are lovers; some are one-night stands. I found I really was the lover, with no desire whatsoever to be a wife. Initially it was wonderful to have Gerald there, but familiarity breeds presumption, the visitor becomes the furniture. The special becomes the everyday. As a mistress, there will be new lingerie (Gerald: *Ooohh, a welcoming party. I see you have put out the bunting*), fresh perfume, make-up, the artifice of love contrived anew, rather as though every time we met was his birthday or some other special day. I could pander to my own exaggerated femininity and almost always be perfectly groomed (though not the day after that day at Ascot, about which I still shudder). I would be there, his lover, his listening post, someone to dine with, always have a glass of something chilled for him, to laugh at his jokes, massage his shoulders, for him to take my hand and show me the stars. I found I was not put on this earth to pick up his socks, have dinner always ready on the table, let the gas man in, placate his children (not that he had any) juggle relationships within a confined space, as indeed wives are consummate heroines and experts at doing. Nor to run his life, that was Wendy's job and exceptionally well she did it too. And about that time, Gerald developed a snore. Not a particularly loud one, but a long drawn-out one. I can see how marriages fail on the rocky boulders of broken sleep; in the orange-tinged, inky

London darkness of my room, I would lie beside him, on the intake of his breath, my hopes would rise; on the out-blowing, with such a fanfare of sound from him, my heart would sink. You could not sleep with that! I would poke him and he would turn over. But night after night of this? No, this was not for me; I learned afresh that the mistress is there, unfashionable as this now is, installed like a plaything, to give all her attention to one man and his whims, be they sexual or otherwise. In this day and age, it seems such a thing of luxury for him. Luxury and the mistress: are they not two matching halves of the same fruit? And for me? Well, I am older and wiser. Then, that was how it was. I was happy, in love and I fitted that role.

I was glad eventually then – indeed secretly and traitorously relieved – as Greg began to mend, to see Gerald move back to his flat, an eyrie in one of the Barbican towers, halfway between the City and the West End, to recover my home, to be able to welcome him after a few days' gap, with the benefit of some personal space and the distance of some private time. Perhaps this is how some marriages function successfully: some wives are like this, when their husbands travel a lot. Mrs W-D perhaps? But that is another sphere, not mine.

Gerald took Greg to all sorts of events, part of broadening his outlook and education. It was good of Gerald to take the time, to give Greg that time and I think Greg appreciated it. Certainly I would have done. They went to all the museums in London, many of the galleries, many of the exhibitions. And they were a very beautiful couple, the elegant, so chic, well-dressed older man, the mane contained (by this time it had recovered from my efforts), and the young boy, well, young man really, well dressed, very tall, blond, the blush of handsome youth in early bloom. For such ventures, Gerald on occasion took to carrying a stick, said it made him feel debonair, and he liked to lean back on it, glasses down his nose, at a painting or a sculpture, fancying himself learned, whilst he held forth to the enraptured Greg.

One day, in the summer of 2002, to kill time before a meeting, I wandered into the Victoria and Albert Museum, that strange collection of all manner of things from all over the world, brought together initially by that Victorian habit of taking whatever you fancy, bringing it home from all the corners of the world and displaying it, as though, because you are British, you have a right to it. Things have moved on since then and, since I was there, I wandered through the Islamic section, past the beautiful Arabic tiles, to look at the clothes of the designer Catherine Walker, who did so much for Princess Diana's look.

It was a separate exhibition, in amongst a wider collection of twentieth-century fashion. The room was darkened, as such displays often are, to protect the clothes, and there were a number of young girls, presumably fashion students, liberally strewn around the exhibits, drawing them. I wandered amongst the displays, reading the explanations, admiring the clothes, joining the students in their breathless awe at the detail and skill in constructing some of the truly outstanding garments.

Sometimes when you are away from someone you love, their scent comes to you on a breeze, as though they were in the room with you, though in reality they are miles away. It may just be a trick of the imagination but this happens a lot with me, and I smiled at the memories, as a very dainty draft brought me the smell of lavender. It is such a familiar smell of course that I thought nothing of it. I wandered around a tall glass cabinet encompassing another wonderful creation, and there, with his back to me was Greg, whilst Gerald, waving his stick around in what he thought of as a tutorial fashion, was standing facing Greg and, thus, me, saying something about the clothes they were looking at.

I froze. Gerald did not. Seeing me, taking me in, he paused, as though drawing a longish breath, and went on. He did not say hello, he did not acknowledge me. He was, however, albeit temporarily, looking straight at me. Greg did not notice the possible break in transmission. I knew for some long, long seconds, something of how Ascot Girl must have felt, that day at the barrier. I was rooted, could not move away. It was not quite how Ascot Girl was passed over all those years before – Gerald had not even drawn breath for her – but for me, in those few frozen seconds, it was still very strange, very uncomfortable.

Gerald still went on talking, still not otherwise acknowledging me. It became very clear, very quickly, that he was not going to. But then, as they began to move off, Gerald winked. A sly wink, a quick wink, the briefest of smiles, then he hurried after Greg, who was pointing to the next dress and called: "Uncle, Uncle Gerald, look at this drapery, what a shape." With the wink, in Gerald's codebook, honour, if not actually done, was seen to be done. By Gerald to me at least. The message was clear, the need was to protect Greg or protect Greg's image of Uncle Gerald. All right then, the truth; to protect Gerald, as he could not bear to dent Greg's hero worship. The sop to me – fool, fool, stupid, foolish, too-loving me – was the wink. As if that made up for being otherwise ignored, unacknowledged, the eternal role of the mistress, to be taken out, used when needed, put away. How absurd was that? But then, who was the fool who made no protest? Then came the letter as though nothing had happened:

> *Yesterday I took Greg my nephew to the Catherine Walker exhibition at the V&A.*

And in the margin, as the afterthought, presumably once Mrs W-D had moved away: *Sweeting, I know you would have loved it!* Loved it? Damn you, Gerald, I was there, I did love it! Till you came along with him! Why couldn't he just acknowledge me in writing, if not in person at the time? Childish isn't it, playground stuff, but I was hurt, rebuffed, despite the wink. The rebel in me – small that it is, part-time that it may be – ground my teeth at this. Gerald's black loopy writing went on, as though nothing had happened.

> *There were four of Princess Diana's dresses there, including the long white/cream one full of pearls and sequins she wore to the Breast Cancer do in the States and the short blue, heavily embossed sleeveless dress she wore to the sale of her dresses. Even though he would have been quite young at the time, Greg remembered them both very well. Both of course were magnificent, particularly the white/cream one. Do you recall them?*

Yes, I remembered it, I remembered you raving about the white/cream one, about how beautiful she was, another woman. Never mind she was a princess. How can

I be bitter about a woman in a photograph – but then, why not?

There were several things from a close inspection that caused Greg to think further. The dresses were both heavily, heavily strewn with pearls and diamonds and sequins and every kind of jewel. They were truly fabulous in their extravagance. Of course, embossed and encrusted as they are, they must be very heavy and Greg wondered how the fabric would stand up to the weight. The dresses were only made to be worn perhaps, at very maximum, half a dozen times, but he was not sure they could have stood up to more than that. Then, both dresses were sleeveless, so that under your arm, as Greg pointed out, you would be rubbing against the decoration all the time. I had never thought about it before. As Greg queried, what would that be like, over the course of an evening? Most uncomfortable I should think.

And on it went.

And surely, as Greg pointed out, it would be impossible to sit down. The dress would be great for standing in and looking stunning, as the flashes of the cameras catch on the sequins et al, but surely to sit down you would leave a settling of broken jewellery. As Greg said, one could hardly fidget, or there would be a snapping of decoration and when you rose, there would be a trail behind you. And if you had a bustle (not that these did), how could you sit down, without crushing it? I think Greg is going to be a very practical designer.

Even the photos of her do not do any justice to the dress. Greg says that it is only when you see it on a mannequin that it is possible to appreciate the detail in the design, much of which is exquisite. Where all that decoration is sewn by hand, which of course in her case it was, what must that cost, and what must that do to the stitcher's eyes and fingers? What a skill to have. Greg was full of admiration. And how painful to create that look. And how do you cut the cloth?

On and on. Greg said this, Greg thinks that. No other words of endearment to me, nothing else personal to me, nothing loving between he, that is, Gerald and I. Where I was not jealous of Max (by then sadly dead), well, of course I was of Greg. If it wasn't Mrs W-D on hand to act as unwitting censor, then it was Greg, damn him! And this is the role of the mistress, to play second, third, fourth fiddle to all comers to one's lover, the role clearly unedifying as I so plainly found it. See how long I took to learn?

In a most unsightly manner (accordingly to Gerald from other occasions), reading the letter alone, I curled my lip and sneeringly muttered the words, "Greg said this, Greg thinks that," as though I was back in the playground, passed over by my best friend for someone else and that could ease my pain. Of course it did not. Nothing could. You might ask why did I stay with him, what small bit of him that I had? I think now that love is like a spider's web; unwittingly, unnoticed, you blunder into the webbing, you get trapped in the sticky gossamer of love and the spider comes out and helps himself to whatever bit of you he wants, as in Gerald's case, your heart and your affections. And then dumps the rest. But perhaps now I am too cynical, perhaps this is unfair. Was it that we were so far downriver, we were trapped within the channelled river walls, the sides too deep then to climb out? Who can say, outside a relationship looking in?

What is true – totally undeniably true, however much it hurts – is that Greg occupied parts of Gerald's heart that I could only dream of. And whilst my heart is big, and I loved Gerald to a fault, tolerating the most humiliating rebuffs, despite that, even I was hurt, having to understand that Greg had to be protected at all costs from the antics, habits and mistress of his hero, Uncle Gerald. So that Gerald would never fall off the pedestal of Greg's adoration, never be made to reap what he had sown. Would he?

There is a sequel to this, also played out at the V&A. Another exhibition, of the Versace portfolio of clothes later the same year, but this time the letter from Gerald came before I went, after he had been to a preview drinks party there, part of a publicity campaign he was running. I went alone. Gerald had exhorted me, in his rollercoaster script:

> *You* MUST *go! They are, well, just wonderful, awesome, amazing, stunning garments. Oh, and self-evident question, why don't they put a mirror behind the models? Clothes you would not be seen dead in, clothes you would not be seen near, clothes you could never even wear for a bet. Not a single item surely would a sane woman crave, but to be sure, they must be seen to be believed.*

This man's style was utter fantasy dressing; he was the Salvador Dalí of cloth. The clothes were almost vulgar, but not in the derogatory sense of the word, more the garish sense. And what was strange is how remember in the eighties the clothes were so shocking but now they are almost a commonplace and de rigueur apparently if you are gay. Vulgar is a good description and certainly so when you think how they were translated from catwalk to street, and what people did to them. There were all those truly ghastly, huge rococo patterns, patterns upon patterns, clash of styles, clash of colours. The clothes are theatrical, like putting a whole play onto someone's back, truly extraordinary. I have spent much of this morning urging all my female friends to go. It is a MUST-see exhibition. You must go! The V&A is open late either Wednesdays or Thursdays, can't remember. It runs till January. Go!

Ignore the bit about "all my female friends". I am sure there were many. It is best not to dwell on what you cannot change. I went. Yes he was right, the clothes were extraordinary, bizarre, out of this world, of their time utterly unprecedented. But even more extraordinary (how unexpectedly prescient Gerald's words were to be), even more unexpected, was the sight of Greg there again, a new Greg, not seen before.

Greg, in leathers, black leathers; the hair not as beautifully combed as many of the photos, or indeed the previous exhibition. Tousled, even perhaps greased in some way, so handsome, he was looking at the mannequins, with another young man. The young man had painted black nails and (as I discovered when he raised his head) mascara. Standing almost hip to hip, their heads were very close together, looking at some detail in the hem of the coat on the model. They were very absorbed, a self-sufficient unit. Or so it looked.

As I passed, ultra-quietly I thought, though it made little difference as there was very heavy rock music overhead, Greg looked up and smiled. Really smiled, like he knew me.

"Hello," he said. "You're Uncle G's—"

Recovering my surprise, automatically I helpfully furnished the word "friend". Young as he was, though by then he must have been about twenty-one, he shouldered that one gratefully.

"Yes," he mused, rolling the phrase around, testing it, "Uncle G's friend," and smiled again, very charmingly. The family likeness to Mrs W-D was remarkable, but warmer, more friendly. Understandably so, really. He introduced me to his "friend", Michael, who then gracefully excused himself, leaning forward, after staring at me, to kiss Greg's cheek before he left. Uncle G? Does no one in that family call each other by their normal name, or was that just Gerald?

At Greg's suggestion, we went to have a cup of tea, that great English stalwart at such times. How do other countries manage without this elixir?

"How did you know who I was?" I stirred the tea.

He smiled, saying, "The photo in his office."

"Would that be the one under the sofa?" I supplied, grinning. I found to my surprise, despite everything that had happened, that I was growing to like Greg. And I knew that my photo had followed the one of Grace and Gerald, under the sofa, in times when it would be awkward to explain it away.

"Why, yes," said he, looking relieved, asking in his turn: "How did you know?"

And we smiled simultaneously. I liked him then, he had such an easy charm, he was no longer a competitor but somehow I suspected we were to be partners in secrets. "Oh, just an educated hunch," I said, and that was it. I did not ask how many other photos he had found there, or of whom. I knew the photo, and I knew that it was sited with discernment and judiciously moved, depending on who came into the office, which was fair enough. And of course, the obvious hiding place was under the sofa. Mrs Oliver – the sainted, sour and peppermint-scented Mrs Oliver – had missed it on her cleaning rounds. And what secrets that sofa holds.

Greg's 'friend' was obviously to be our secret, just as our meeting was to be another, from Gerald. Greg acknowledged Gerald's conspiracy, to keep me from him: "I knew you were there, behind the scenes, so to speak," he said. "I don't know why he pretends we don't know. Uncle G is well known in the family for his love of a pretty woman." See the charm, the tact, not bad for a twenty-one-year-old man and an apparently gay one at that. I blushed suitably at that one. I wanted to add *and his inability to pass one by*, but this was Greg, Gerald's Greg. I was imbued with Gerald's need to protect him, even then. "And I knew you at the Catherine Walker exhibition," he went on. "I knew it was you, it just did not need to be announced." And I smiled at that (see the sops that I was happy to receive?), that there was something between Gerald and I that could not be ignored. Sad really, but not then, not when Greg said it. I did not stop to think that of course he knew me from the photograph, not an imagined crackle in the air between Gerald and I. How blinkered a lover is, how desperate.

We parted after about an hour, carrying our secrets. His, that I was Gerald's mistress, mine that he was gay. Uncle G apparently did not know about Greg's Michael, or indeed any of the others – well, I knew that he did not know. Gerald – Uncle Gerald the Stud – would not be able to willingly cope with such a detail about his Greg whom, it goes almost without saying, he adored, and for whom, of all the people Gerald knew, Gerald would go to the ends of the earth for. Greg's being gay just did not fit into Gerald's view of how things were. With a final very beautiful smile, Greg asked me to be discreet.

"Our secret?" he asked.

"Our secret," I promised. Then we shook hands, rather formally. "We never met?" I suggested.

"Agreed," said he, with a firm handshake. The secrets were just between us. Safe.

But making this a triumvirate of secrets, Greg about me, mine about Greg, there would be, of course, another. It would be a long way in the future, to neatly seal the triangle, between Gerald and I, but in the circumstances, Greg was never to know what happened. Only I would know, and Mrs W-D, outside that particular triangle, would guess. Because unless you are there, the facts can only be surmised. Or covered up.

14

An Evening of Artistry

Gerald liked to think of himself as a patron of the arts. I say it in this way because really to him art was a connection, another route to bring people together, rather than for him to enjoy, say, a painting in its own right. A new sculptor, a new painter would consider themselves very lucky if they attracted the attention of Gerald Wendon-Davis, as the influence and connections of Wendon-Davis Associates could then open doors, provide hanging spaces, put noughts on the end of prices. After all, those walls in all those offices in the City have to be filled by something.

In the jargon of marketing, as Gerald would put it, he was a good early adopter, he could predict a trend, spot a change in direction. And Gerald could sell the Emperor his new clothes. Well, not sell, it was not an occupation Gerald would acknowledge, more that Gerald would persuade the Emperor of the future investment potential of, say, a canvas all but blue, except for a strip of red down one side. And more remarkably, get an advance order for next year's portfolio of paintings. Very often I could not see the art, and

I suspect neither could Gerald, but he could persuade you it was there. And to your surprised pleasure, looking at the canvas again and again, seeing whatever Gerald had found there, you would reach for your cheque, or later for your credit card. To the artist, who swallowed all the charming patter, that was what mattered. To Gerald, he had brought people together, made new connections, reinforced those already made, for future connections. It was all stashed away, that information. Information… for Gerald, in making his connections, information was a lifeblood.

An artistic evening was always heralded by a white card invitation. To think that once, years and years ago, I was impressed, thrilled by such things. It is true that they were very smart. Mine for Ascot – what a long time ago that was and I still shudder, but no matter – graced the mantelpiece for all the days between receiving it and the day. I can't call it the big day anymore. Before the day, I drew everyone's attention to it, it was so exciting. Afterwards, well, who knows what happened to it.

The card for the artistic evening arrived in a very white thick envelope. There was the usual *Wendon-Davis Associates invites* and then the name of the invitee. Gerald had not written mine this time, his long-suffering secretary Wendy had. On the invitation I received for Ascot, above the printed *Wendon-Davis Associates requests the pleasure of…* Gerald had written, *It is with very great pleasure that…* He had not written anything like that on this occasion. Was I moving down the scale from the organ grinder to the monkey? But no, I think that now; then I don't think I would have noticed. But Gerald had written on the bottom of the card in between the RSVP and the *Dress Code: Lounge Suits*, in his loopy handwriting, *Looking forward to seeing you!* and I took heart from that.

The setting was underground, in a huge restaurant in Covent Garden. It was shortly after Bill Clinton had testified to the grand jury about his "inappropriate intimate contact" with Monica Lewinsky in mid-August 1998. There had been much joking during the day about what constituted 'inappropriate'.

Thankfully it was not a themed evening, where unsuspecting, non-playing guests are surprised (and often appalled) to be drawn into a game for which they have no appetite and no interest. Gerald did have more sense than that. The room, well, a barn of a room really, was white, with brilliant lights, searing glare into corners. There were pictures everywhere; I could hear mutters of "the next Damien Hirst" or "a follow-up to Tracey Emin" amongst the guests, as well as discussion of Bill Clinton's 'inappropriate behaviour'. All the arty press were there, whom Gerald in rash moments on paper had described as "The great unwashed, they of the great pretensions, directing the buying public with a pomposity that defies description." This particular evening, I thought they looked quite clean and respectable. Everyone had mobile phones, many of which were clamped to their ears, and everyone clearly knew a lot of "Darlings".

To say the canvases were dreadful is to dignify them with something they had no right to, give them a definition. They were shameful, appallingly bad. I was surprised at Gerald, normally such an arbiter of good taste, style, recognising the next truly great work of art before it became public. This was not it. It was when I saw the artist that I understood Gerald's apparent failure of judgement.

Here, I should just add something. Gerald had impeccable manners. He was not thoughtless. He had written on my invitation: *Looking forward to seeing you!* And I know that he meant it. Clearly all those hours with Nanny had worked. Such genuine communication skills. But there was just one small gap, where Nanny's admonitions, directions, praise, discipline could never, in her wildest dreams, have reached. I think this particular area would never have occurred to her. Imagine a child at table and all is well, his manners are perfect. Then someone brings in a wonderful cake. The cake is sliced. And the child, reaching forward, perhaps muttering under his breath, 'Mine!' reaches, before anyone else can move, for the largest slice, or the bit with the biggest cherry. And this was Gerald. He might have had the first course and minded his manners (did Mrs W-D mind being described as a first course?), and the second and done the same (me), but that did not hold him back when it came to dessert (all the other women out there). The cherry on the cake.

And here was the latest. She was, well, the usual, really. Gerald had espied the artistry in the artist. There was no failure of judgement on his part; her canvases were just a part of the package. Never mind he would be the only beholder, here was art. Young, long dark hair, huge eyes, very golden-brown, smooth, supple skin, the mystery of a young animal. She was long-limbed, the bloom of love and trust all over her, wholly captivated by Gerald's charm. Inexplicably, she was dressed as a Native American, or something very similar, and her hand was on Gerald's arm, rather like a kestrel sitting on the leather fittings covering the wrist of its handler. Waiting for instructions to fly. Had she a name yet? The Lure?

Gerald was in his element. Deep amongst the crowd of his H&H crowd (Gerald-ese for hail and hearties, or FOGs – Friends of Gerald, my term), much laughter, many friends, much imbibing, lots of fun, he was introducing the latest catch. For her, I knew the violins were playing, her feet were dancing, the candles were sparking. Were they already beginning the waltz together? *Welcome to the seraglio*, thought I, looking at her in the spotlight of Gerald's enchantment. It would be an evening for her that would set her alight; it would stand for the rest of her life as a high spot and few other nights would match it. Afterwards – wiser, hurt – she might shake her head in wonderment at her innocence, but then, that night, the future was ahead of her and just then it was rose-tinted, glowing, warm, happy, terribly happy. The musicians in her head had only just begun their night's work. The reach of the tide remains the same whatever else happens afterwards. As does the telltale stain mark, where the tide has been.

And Gerald? The old *roué*, he was alight with pleasure at the sight of his friends shaking their heads with envy. Never mind she was half his age, never mind to some he was a dirty old man; he was something, "that Gerald", to chuckle over, slightly envious. And of course, all those H&Hs, of course they would want to be where he was, or, so they imagined, he would be later.

The evening wore on. He was a king amongst his courtiers. In another time, he would have been the Sun King, the absolute monarch, radiant in brocade and ribbon, amongst the mirrors at Versailles. Even here, underground in London on a rainy evening, he was incandescent, the God of Love, aflame with power, glorious in his pleasure, luminous in his belief that another innocent was to be added to the Collection, what he liked to call the Salon of Venus (another of Gerald's "witticisms"). Strutting his stage, he was brimful of largesse, bonhomie, distributor of sperm (though Gerald would not say this, I say it now). Peeping, what he would believe was inconspicuously, at his reflection in those paintings that had been framed and glazed, he revelled in what he saw and the vision of young loveliness beside him, 'collected' for later delectation.

By then, Gerald's hair was white and very distinguished. He was not looking bad really, the mane aflame in the glaring lights, making him the centre of the room, the star attraction. Tony had done well. My efforts with the hair remover had left no lasting effect, the Style now long forgotten. Perhaps the chins were starting to run amok then, the growing waistline still well-tailored over. And my role in all this? From my watching role from the distant side of the room, caught between one dreadful picture after another, murmuring hellos to people I knew, nodding at slight acquaintances, being introduced to others, I did have time to wonder, was my position from now on to be that of a kind of older Madame de Pompadour (albeit I was mixing the relationships of my King Louis's, *père* and *fils*), now friend and confidante to the King, but no longer sharing the King's bed, whilst he sought solace in the secrets of younger flesh, more flexible limbs, his aging desire set aflame by the energies of younger women? A woman next to me, who presumably had not succumbed to his charms, saw me looking at him and muttered: "Look at him, it's disgusting. Dirty old man. He's quite old enough to be her father." Then, sensing sympathy, she went on: "Talk about trying to put old wine in a new bottle." Even I was taken aback at that one.

Across the room, Gerald, oblivious to all else for a moment, turned to the Lure. She turned to him, by now dancing like a filly fresh out of the stable, full of fireworks in her toes. He kissed her on the lips. I have written this in such a blunt way. When lovers kiss, they turn into each other, into and creating a secret world. For the inhabitants of that secret world all else stops, time, noise, awareness of other people. So it was here. She raised her face to his, rather as a sunflower seemingly tracks the path of the sun. She raised her face to his, I could see a smile playing over her lips, an anticipatory, sensual smile. She would be looking into the lambency of his eyes… just as I have done, thousands of times, in just such circumstances. He leaned forward, his scent washing gently over her, as it had me... He was presumably smiling too. The mole beside his eye would be riding the tossing waves of crinkled skin. I have seen that smile a thousand, thousand times, very deliberate, playful, moving deliberately to the kill. In films, the man looks into the woman's eyes, then, at the last minute, his eyes drop to her lips, before his eyes close, succumbing to the impact of the kiss. Gerald did not do that, his eyes would stay fixed on yours, till his lips met yours, enhancing the effect of the swoop… to the kill… and then he would almost swoon as he succumbed. Or so it would appear. I have seen this time beyond number or measure. I wonder now if he practised this move before the mirror. Certainly the first time I experienced it, it was startling, but then perhaps that was intended. You were startled but then the impact of his lips would startle you more. Or that was the general idea.

No time to dwell on this now. Back to the kiss. Presumably this swooning he did. Her eyes were shut, she saw none of this.

Their lips met. The world was silent to them as they touched. It was not particularly passionate, not to an observer, but inside the secret world, much is promised, much left unsaid, hanging in the air between them like electricity before a thunderstorm, the pulses race, anticipation is all, many hares are set running.

The pain it caused me, a terrible thing, caused me to gasp, so that the woman who had tutted over the disparity between their ages, half-turned to see that I was all right. It was like a stab in the heart, of betrayal, of terrible jealousy, of instability, of rejection, perhaps all of these things. The bile rose in my throat. The anger, the rage, the terrible, terrible envy. Briefly in my pain, I dropped my eyes to shield myself from the sight, but then, macabre as it may seem, I had to turn back, drawn like a magnet to look at Gerald. And because he was attached to her, to her too, the Lure. They were drawing apart, slowly, reluctantly, as if the magnet that had brought them together was something they had to fight against in order to separate for now. And return to later, privately, uninhibitedly. I saw her face flush with pleasure as her head came clear from Gerald's and she was looking at him with stars in her eyes, oblivious for a few seconds more to the rest of the room. Then the hubbub of the room penetrated – for of course it had never stopped – and Gerald stepped back, safe in the knowledge that her eyes would follow him. Lovers betray all their secrets, especially the ones really in love, really trapped. In that moment, she did. And she was.

For the rest of the evening, for which, remarkably, I stayed, as the wine flowed, the conversation rose and fell, believe it or not, such was the power, the force of Gerald, that some of the dreadful paintings were sold. Little red spots began to appear beside ghastly pictures, ridiculous prices. The young and very lovely artist fluttered around Gerald. She shimmered at his urging. He displayed her, soothed her, charmed her. It was very practised. The press surged and flowed, as did the H&Hs. Cheques discreetly changed hands with the business cards, the language of connection. Occasionally, he would look over to me, where I was wandering around the room, and he would wink or nod when he saw me talking to people I knew. Would Gerald leave with her, having spent the evening with her? Very unlikely, given his track record. The moment of him breaking her heart was drawing near.

It so happened I had tablets for constipation in my bag. This picture stays in my mind. There is Gerald, with the press mobbing him, she, the latest lovely, clamped to his side. I know Gerald has next day's papers in his mind and the headline, *Wendon-Davis spots a winner again*, just as though she were his next racehorse. The tablet came into my hand. I knew one, just one alone was very strong. And for a man for whom the free movement of his bowels is as though breathing…

There is a God. He often looks away at the important times in life and lets you learn how to get on with things. I am now an expert in this.

Gerald came by. Smiling his 'good to see you' sort of smile, accompanied by the blank look 'but I can't remember your name' above it. Remember, I have known him for years. He was so close, he could not miss me without being terribly rude. Gerald was not rude.

"Sweeting!" he cried, as if he had just spotted me. "How nice you could make it."

I leaned forward. "I would not have missed it. For the world," I murmured, which was, in the circumstances, going a bit far but nonetheless Gerald said nothing and we air-kissed. You do in public, whatever your relationship is, or maybe has been. Especially with the new string to the bow in sight, as well as the world's – well, London and New York's – assembled press. And I dropped the tablet. As luck would have it, it fell into the glass. And fizzed in the champagne. There is a God, the God of Quiet Satisfactions. Gerald retreated and, looking a little bashful – he knew that I knew about her, all about her – said, waving his glass, but not – I was amazed to see – not really studying it to see what had happened, "See, Sweeting, you still make my bubbles fizz." Which for Gerald was actually quite funny. The bubbles did fizz. Almost to the top of the glass, which might have diluted the tablet but no, the bubbles subsided.

Just then, a young girl came by with a tray of canapés. Perhaps it was her first job. Of all the people in the room, she was the most self-absorbed, in that way that the newly adult have, and she had no idea who Gerald was. She was blonde, with, what Gerald would describe as a sumptuous figure, all in black velvet, very curvy, the material stretching as though plastered on to her generously angled body, built, in Gerald's words, "For comfort, not speed." The depth of her cleavage was lost amid the spotlights as she moved across the room, but the curve of each breast was clearly delineated against the black cloth. There was a mole on one, very close to the bottom of the V of her dress. Espying it, a light had come into Gerald's eye. A look of sheer lubricity came over his face. He could not turn away from her, even if his life depended upon it. She for him at that moment was his North Pole, he was (in his mind at least) her magnet. His face was an advertising board announcing an empty space in his bed for her if she played her cards right. I know the expression and, in the shadow of her youth and considerable all-too-visual curvaceous charms, I knew he had forgotten me standing next to him.

Gerald smiled at her, his 'I'm a bit of a boy'-type smile, forgetting completely he was old enough to be her father and she, apparently touched at his attention, smiled back, basking in his warmth. She had deeply blue eyes, probably ably assisted by contact lenses. Gerald, apparently oblivious to me standing next to him, was almost unable to help himself; he was like a dog with a bone, agog at her prettiness. And that figure. He was just salivating at the thought of an hour, two hours, more if possible, spent as close as possible to that skin. Sounds awful that I know such things… disgusting, perhaps? I had known him too long not to know what he was thinking. Apart from anything else, I could see his all-too-apparent reaction. Had I not been there, I just know he would have asked for her number. Even with that age difference.

That evening's selection of canapés were rather unusual and Gerald asked her what this particular tray was.

"Them's tiny Yorkieee puds," she replied in best shrill Estuary English, all the way from parts east of London.

"My favourite," Gerald assured her, smiling deeply into her eyes. Leaning slightly towards her, "You could feed it to me, if you wanted to," he drawled, sidling up to her, so that they became joined at the hip. He reminded me of a crab, who has not seen a potential mate, oh, for at least a millennium. His smile grew more languid, waiting. My presence was all too clearly forgotten.

"Not likely, mate," she said drawing herself and her impressive bosom up and, in the same movement, taking herself away from his hip. "Vat's dirty, 'innit!" She even managed to look affronted at his suggestion, but she held her tray of canapés firmly under his nose.

At her rejection, Gerald did not even look abashed. He rather meekly helped himself to a 'pud'. Forgetting, or indeed unaware that you should not mention such things to men who look deep into your eyes in that particular way that Gerald had, however old they are, she smiled again and said: "Yeah," she sighed, steadying herself for the shot, "them's my ole dad's favourite too." There was a second's hush in our trio. It was suddenly enormously tempting to me to laugh. Perhaps her old dad had, after all, told her how to treat men like Gerald. As she turned away, having dropped her bombshell, I bit my lip, managing to withhold the smile as Gerald grimaced to her retreating back and all-too-lovely curved bottom.

As she moved away, I, being well versed in that notion women have that they should protect their men however badly or stupidly their men behave, began: "But you don't like—" and he, coming back to himself, finished: "Yes, I hate 'em," and turning to me, "but you know how I hate to disappoint," all Mr Smoothie, winking at me. "What shall I do with it now?" he wondered and, reaching over without further discussion, he delved into the nearest flower arrangement with it, a florist's contortion of stems and petals, on the occasional table just beside us. "There," he said, leaning forward to leave the pudding amid the petals, so that it looked like an opening flower. Then standing back near me, his scent of lavender washing gently over me, he put his head on one side to survey his handiwork and said: "I think that rather nicely deals with that, don't you?"

Composed again, we stood together and surveyed the room, or rather I did and thus unabashed, as though the incident had simply never happened, Gerald looked at the Lure, Georgie, I think her name was. Eventually, according to one of the gossip diaries, she came out as a lesbian, except that apparently it was all for publicity, not honesty's sake (according to Gerald, blithely disregarding any feelings or interest I might have had on the matter), before shunning London life for an island in Scotland, with all the dreadful paintings. She was even too alternative for what had become known as Brit Art but her art was as awful. This night, as we watched, she shimmered with one of the H&Hs who had made her laugh at his comment. She put back her head and her neck was long, firm and unlined. I never even thought about putting my hands around it. She was not the problem. We looked on. She was lovely, her skin supple with the glow of youth, being in love, being admired and apparent impending success. I began to feel very old. There was no threat of double chins on the horizon just then for her, no crinkled top lip from too much kissing or even pursing with disapproval. Her long hair shone in the brilliant lights. Beside me, Gerald sighed. "Isn't she lovely," he murmured, salivating slightly, as though I were his madame, keeper of the brothel, not his long-time mistress of many years standing. "The show's going rather well, don't you think, Sweeting?" He sipped his champagne thoughtfully. Remarkably there was no sign of the tablet in it.

Next day, it was difficult to determine the art from the effect of the tablet. It could be construed as an early example, I suppose, of male date rape, except that that evening Gerald did not manage the date nor was he raped. He was taken advantage of, but not in a way he might have wished. I left just before the tablet made its speedy impact. About the same time or earlier, women in nightclubs had been warned, and would learn to guard their glasses against such invasion and even to drink directly from the bottle. Gerald had not learned of this then.

The publicity of Gerald's sudden collapse and departure was good but not a high spot for Gerald, certainly not what he may have had in mind. Next day's headline gossip writers excelled themselves. *Gerald Wendon-Davis sick of art.* I would discover later Gerald wanted to sue over this one. Presumably the artist was holding out on him. It was a Herculean task indeed to decide on my favourite. *Wendon-Davis sickened at art show* was a particular delight. *MP's husband taken ill by painting* was special. I cut it out for the wall in my kitchen. It made me laugh out loud. There were no pictures and the kestrel-like girl – poor girl – had a mention, but not a kind one. Something like, *Evening pales for young artist.*

There is a bit more to this story. Revenge, as they say, is a dish best served cold. I have said that I left before the deluge. I stood outside, and after about thirty minutes a taxi was called to the back door. How did they get Gerald out you may wonder, but I do not want to dwell on that. Gerald and the Kestrel, or the Lure, or whatever he called her, got into a taxi and I heard her give the address, clearly across the evening air: "15 The Mews, off Curzon Street, W1." Off went the taxi. Urgently.

I got into one behind. There is nothing quite like the pleasure of giving instructions, paying for them in person, to see them carried out perfectly. We drove down Curzon

Street, to the mews where lights were being thrown on all over the place. What a night ahead of them. Quite different from Gerald's intentions.

Nearby after a little reconnoitre, I found several Indian restaurants, and then a kebab café and a pizza house. From each of them, alternating meals from different continents were ordered. Every hour, through the night till dawn, a very smelly, very strong full meal would be sent out, to 15 The Mews, off Curzon Street, W1. Unordered by the inhabitants – one of them very ill and totally uninterested in food – the meals would punctuate the small hours, the smell, garlicky, spicy, greasy, and all-pervading would filter up the stairs, seeping through the air of the flat, uninvited, unwanted, uneaten. Imagine that on a rebelling stomach. The noise of their arrival by those untended, clanking exhausts on the old jalopy cars such restaurateurs like to deliver in – or those whiney motorbikes delivery boys use – and the refusal of the food by No. 15 would keep the neighbours from sleep. And to compound the felony, a taxi would arrive on the half hour, apparently ordered by the inhabitants of No. 15. The noise of its diesel engine arriving, idling, turning and leaving would be cursed by all parties.

I wonder now if Mrs W-D smiled to herself at the news. Funny to have a sense of *esprit de corps* with the wife of your lover. Did he tell her what had befallen him, up to the detail of with whom he left the restaurant, of course? The press was quite comprehensive on the story, again up to the point Gerald left the restaurant. I would like to have shared the *après-ski* detail with her. One should, after all, enjoy the occasional victory, small and rare as they may be. And from wherever they come.

15

The Last Straw

When did I decide I would try to kill him? Had Mrs W-D gone down this road and discounted it for the scandal? Was I doing her a favour?

In those days, before I met Gerald – and because it was what you did – I had a vibrator. It helped take the edges off life, bring a rosy tint to dreadful days. Then I was Miss-I-will-not-be-impaled. The butterfly eluding the net. The Collector came upon it one day (did I unconsciously call him that?). "What's this for, my girl?" said he, waving it in the air, as though he wanted to beat me with it. "Ho, ho, we can have some fun with this." But we never did, I did not impale myself. I may have stabbed him, but he brought it upon himself, made me do it. Indeed, in the light of what happened, induced me to do it. But there I go, getting ahead of myself again.

So this day I came home to the flat, letting myself in and promising myself a cup of tea. It was a Monday in mid-October 2002; I had managed to change the bed that morning before leaving, but not move all the Sunday papers after Gerald's trawling through them the day before. It had not been a good Sunday for Gerald, not many of his leads and hints about his clients were in. Instead, there were headlines about love triangles between two Swedes and an Italian, one of the Swedes being the English national football team coach, the other a television personality; the shock waves were still reverberating after Mrs Barrymore's revelations about her husband's swimming talents, Edwina Currie's clanger about her relationship with John Major and, finally, if such were needed, ongoing discussions about Angus Deayton and the merits of who should replace him on his weekly satirical programme. Gerald had mumbled and cursed a lot and even managed to knock a potted plant over before finally leaving the previous evening. I did wonder if maybe he was losing his apparently heretofore magical touch with the press. I had not said this, of course, saying only, "Some you win, some you lose," at the time, which normally Gerald might have said himself. Gerald had only muttered in response. One breath of fresh air had been a photo of the new Conservative Party chair's shoes; Theresa May had worn leopard skin winkle-pickers – Gerald liked sexy shoes. "Shoes say a lot about a woman, Sweeting," he would often opine in happier moments. And of course, he was right.

I could hear classical music, not this time in my imagination; the radio was on. Had I forgotten to turn it off? I stopped and sniffed the air. Crushed lavender and freshly cut grass. Gerald was there! (Tony from Brighton via Jermyn Street must have made up a fresh brew. No one else wore that particular blend of aftershave.) What a nice surprise! He must have let himself in. *We'll have a glass of wine on the balcony*, thought I, mentally changing all sorts of plans. The flat, as I have said, is not that big. I went through towards the kitchen, passing under the gallery, which leads off the upstairs bedroom. The scent was stronger. And there was another smell, a chemically smell, such as women often wore on the Underground in the mornings. Gerald would have called it something horrid, but my mind was so tuned in to seeing him, my pleasure so great, I could not quite imagine the word. Perhaps, I mused, semi-consciously, Tony has put something else in the brew. No matter, I would see him, Gerald, only seconds from now, and he would say whatever the word was and it would be perfect.

So, after putting my things in the kitchen, my heart fluttering – remember what I have said about lovers and how they flush with anticipation at sight of each other – up the stripped pine stairs I went, to the landing, and I turned the door-handle to the bedroom. It was empty. The huge circular westward-facing window showed the sun beginning to sink behind clouds. The smell, now combining, was very strong. *Tony, what else did you put in it?* No Gerald. But the bed, my beautiful bed, my Egyptian white cotton sheets, my wonderful embroidered pillowcases, my crisp, newly ironed duvet, all of it fresh on that morning, all of it was crumpled, overwrought, raped. An elephant had clearly had a fight in it. The music was rising to a crescendo. I crept to the bed. What could have happened?

When lovers have loved long, they know all the intimate things about each other. How each smells first thing in the morning, after a bath, after eating garlic, chilli, curry (Gerald does not eat chilli – *cowboys do*). They know the changes in scent for each part of the day, how soap reacts on the other's skin, what bottled perfume does in combination with its natural counterpart. Particularly that produced after sex. Coming together, as Gerald liked to put it.

I dropped to my knees. I am still disgusted to record what I did next. Would I describe this as the high tide of humiliation? Wouldn't you? I leaned forward, to sniff the sheets, missing by inches, less than that, a long smear of semen. I have said lovers learn to recognise each other's scents and yes, I knew Gerald's. It was the crowning tsunami wave of degradation. None greater. To kneel, in your own bedroom, to discern the sheets on your bed, sullied, besmirched, by another woman's husband (albeit you and he have been lovers for years), after he has been there, uninvited, with yet another woman. The ignominy. It is a shortish, brutish word but it covers such a terrible shame. Even now I shudder to remember.

The phone rang. Picking it up, actress to the last, I drew a deep breath, from somewhere near the raging fires in my bowels. If Mrs W-D could compose her pinked lips into something stiff and unbitten, and that to meet the assembled press at the farm gate, all those years ago, so could I. "Yes?" I said.

"Evelyn?" queried a crisp female voice. And as such is my name, though Gerald would only ever write it in the travelogues, I said: "Yes." Not quite so equally crisply, but not bad in the circumstances. And her voice? Her voice was just as smooth as the television's, the radio's, as familiar to me as mine, as my mother's, as Gerald's. I had known it and heard it for years.

"Evelyn, it is Phyllis Wendon-Davis here." Just like that. No time for me to draw breath, no time to raise my hand to my mouth in horror. Or wonderment. From whence had she got my number?

"Evelyn," she said, as though nothing had happened, the bottom had not dropped out of my thinking brain, the world had not swayed on its axis, the sun was not wobbling about in the sky. "We haven't met but Gerald tells me that you are writing a book. About Suffolk, isn't it, Suffolk churches? And he is helping you. Have you seen Gerald today?" Just like that. Rather as though she might have said: "Hello, it's Phyllis here. Have you seen my glasses?" As though we were sort of chums. A book? What was that about? But there was no time to wonder.

"No," I began to say, what else could I say? She had rather a nice voice. My very first thought was that I wanted to tell her about the awful thing that had just happened to me, how my heart was beginning to crumble, the onset of the chill of nuclear winter on the horizon. I wanted to cry out to her, after all she was another human being, she would understand. *Someone has been sleeping in my bed, who carries no resemblance at all to Daddy Bear but seems to have let himself in, enjoyed an afternoon of delights, availed himself with someone else, of the quiet calm of my home, raped my sheets, wrecked my heart, and was in the process of somehow from a distance stopping my life beat and the blood pulsing in my veins.* But no, I had not seen her husband and I had not got her glasses. Or the other way around. And instead of all that, I dredged from the last vestige of civilisation before the fires inside me overtook it, some recognition that she was, after all, who she was. Mrs Gerald Wendon-Davis. And I was who I was. Gerald's mistress. As deceived, as cheated as she was but without the wedding ring. What he had given to me, indeed to her, he had given to this girl, in my bed. Remarkably, I heard myself go on to say, in really quite a good stab at my normal voice: "I've been out today, to the new exhibition at the Tate."

Now I had put a curtain across the shelves where the previous resident "Madam" had kept her extraordinary and presumably working shoes. And now there was a hanging space behind the curtain for my clothes. Just then the curtain to my wardrobe moved. Rather like the theatre curtain as the play goes on in true farce. The curtain drew back. Was there a roll of drums? There was Gerald. Gerald. Gerald, looking, it must be said, as flustered as I have ever seen him. That is to say, he was in the process of tucking in his shirt. Not the most crisp shirt I have ever seen him attempt to tuck in. And a girl with him, standing beside him. A woman actually. As different from me as it is possible to be.

Part of my mind also registered that she was different from Mrs W-D – well, Phyllis, as I was apparently being invited to call Gerald's wife – who was still on the end of my phone. For one thing, the girl did not wear bright-green suits or grey twin sets and pearls. She had leather trousers on. I think she was even wearing a pair of Manolos, very high, very sexy, very, very expensive. Gerald must have had a field day with his fantasies. Before I came home of course. And her hair, it was like a curtain of red velvet. No wonder he had fallen for her. Later, I would find strands of it on the pillow.

Before me, the two lovers were bending together, 'still dancing', as Gerald had called it sometimes. It is the language of love, played out in their bodies, so that even after sex – because let's be frank, that's what it was – lovers occupy the same aura, the same personal space, until normal life intrudes and the 'bubble' that they occupy, for want of a better word, divides. I could see that she was in the process of putting out a hand, reaching for him, an instinctive grasp, a sort of silent cry – *where you have loved, now protect me* – going up. Protect me against your lover? In her flat? Charming.

But my mind was running on. Mrs W-D was in the middle of saying something futile like 'Oh, how nice'. But funnily, my mind was not really on her response. In those speeded-up processes where you think a thousand thoughts in a second, I noted that she – the girl in my wardrobe with Gerald – was very tall, young (of course), very pretty (what else?), her lips shaped in almost a perfect 'O' (of shock, horror? No pleated top lip there yet, I noted), a redhead with large green blobs for eyes, and, at that moment, she had a rather red face. And there were some other bits of her that were a bit red – I watched them go red – that normally only her husband-to-be – or presumably, Gerald that afternoon – would see. Usually in a paler version. If Gerald had his name for me, what would he call her? Not my special name, not mine. 'Red', probably, yes, that was probably what he would christen her. Gerald would give everyone a special name. And write their given name at the top of the travel letters. And invitations on white card.

Not much later, I would see her photographed in a wedding dress, with an Honourable Somebody, their apparent pleasure in each other that day frozen for all time amid rose petal confetti and rice, in a magazine. Apparently, according to the magazine, her name was Abigail and she was related to a large fortune in shipping. Later still, Gerald would narrowly miss being cited in her divorce proceedings. It would not be one of his best connections. I used the photo for darts practice, up against the kitchen door. Not that I played darts previously but it gave me a peculiar pleasure, totally unforeseen, to stab her beauty over and over again with the point of the dart.

All this passed in a flash. The other part of my mind began to panic, to crave that longed-for moment in the nightmare when you begin to move, to awaken, to lie back in bed exhausted from a sleep that has not refreshed. As you numbly lie there, battered from your own imagination, the tears begin to dry, stiffening your cheeks like a mask, as you comfort yourself – opening your eyes properly – that it was only a nightmare. Conscious and in daylight, you can laugh at your own fears. But it was not to be.

"If you see him," Phyllis went on, as though an earthquake had not just rocked her footings, which of course they had not – for her, presumably all this had happened years ago – "do get him to give me a ring. There is a little difficulty about this evening."

Gerald was smiling sheepishly. A little difficulty about this evening. What about now? My world was caving in around me, my lovely, my oh-so-special home had been invaded, used as a brothel, but still I was standing and apparently acting like a normal human being, holding the phone to Gerald's wife and assessing Gerald's latest piece. And Mrs W-D was worried about this evening. Not the here and now. Why, oh why couldn't I wake up and it all be a bad dream?

"Yes, Mrs Wendon-Davis, I mean Phyllis..." I started to say. Hearing this and realising, Gerald managed to rock back on his heels. I could not look at his eyes. I was aware, such a sharp awareness, out of the corner of my eye, that his skin was taut, pulled, rather like a facelift, back over his cheek bones. Distantly I wondered, was this sort of thing better for him than cosmetic surgery?

A thousand times Gerald has been in my flat, a thousand times he must have passed that curtain without incident. This time, as he moved out of the wardrobe, he must have trodden on the edge of the curtain. With a gentle rustle, barely discernible above the music, the whole curtain fell, *whoossh.* It draped itself over his shoulder and round his body, like a Roman senator's toga. On any other occasion, he and I would have laughed till we howled. Like the time in the tailor's – once I had recovered from the shame of it all – over a glass of wine.

I bit my lip, forcing back the warning words of reaction. *Et tu, Evelyn, my old lovely?* came unbidden into my tortured mind, plagiarising Gerald and Julius Caesar via Shakespeare in one fell swoop, but I could say nothing. The phone was clasped to my ear, Gerald's lawfully married and very legal wife on the other end. She was chattering about something inconsequential. I have forgotten the substance of it, assuming I heard it in the first place. Gerald stood in front of me politely, very handsome, rather worried, shrouded in curtain material. Oh, for a dagger then. What a sweet and timely retribution. It would have been most meet and seemly. See the knife-edge between laughter and tears. And such tears, such tears I would cry. Later, alone, very terribly alone.

The Abigail-person hardly registered what had happened, her eyes were glued to the floor, possibly with shame. I like to think so, to try to credit her with something. Gerald stepped out of the toga, picked up the curtain, rather like Richard Gere at the end of *An Officer and a Gentleman* sweeps up his lady love, off her feet into his arms, off to their happy ending together. Not for us. This time, with the curtain in his arms, Gerald's eyes were asking – as he clearly could not say anything his wife might hear down the phone – where he should put the curtain. I waved to the bed whilst still holding the phone. Perhaps I should have forgotten Mrs Phyllis, or whatever her name was, and clubbed him with the phone there and then. And I watched, whilst Gerald – re-enacting the altar boy from his childhood before the altar – gratefully laid the curtain down, reverently, gently, on the bed presumably in just the same manner as he had laid the girl there earlier in the afternoon.

I moved down the stairs and managed, straining at the phone cord, to open the front door, the phone still clamped to my ear. The phone had been fitted in the days before mobile phones or those phones you can walk round the house with. I had had an exceptionally long cord fitted to it. Just for such occasions, you might now think. And I pointed to the door. Would you believe, would you really believe here, I just pointed to the door? And I finished the sentence to the phone. "Yes, I will tell him." Abigail, with several items of clothing in her hand, went out of it, picking her coat off the hook as she went. Gerald scurried after her, like a rat, still fumbling with his shirt. I noticed even so he managed to pull the door quietly shut. Practice, obviously. "Goodbye Mrs… Phyllis," said I, as my heart broke with a terrible clang, severed and broken in several places.

The orchestra playing the classical music must by now be playing their socks off. Clearly the musicians were approaching new heights. Uninterrupted and egged on by the music, Gerald might have now recovered himself sufficiently to reach another climax. Certainly the violinists were. On other occasions where we were laughing together, I might have teased him that on a good day and a following wind, certain pieces of classical music helped. Beethoven's '1812' was a particular favourite of his. "All that banging, eh?" he would twinkle at me. But not now. Not at that particular moment.

This day, the music heightened to a crescendo, rather like the background to a bad film. I turned it off. There was such a silence. The smell was awful. The wine forgotten, the phone cord still unused for the practical purpose I might otherwise have availed of it, I went to the balcony. I threw open the windows. No, not to throw myself off, no, to go to the edge and throw down his shoes. His very expensive, handcrafted, hand-stitched, personally lasted kid leather shoes. I felt personally lasted. I did not wait for him to get to the bottom or for him to realise he did not have his shoes on. Dimly, I wondered, how had he got his socks on so quickly? Was that the Italian again with the fast getaway in him? Had he not taken them off? I threw the shoes, apparently narrowly missing him, had I stopped to look. Why, how had I missed?

You can see I was in shock. From under the sink, I found rubber gloves. I picked up every last piece of that once-virginal, once-so-beautiful bedding and I tore it off the bed, the gloves shielding my hands but not my heart. And I burned it, I took it to a rubbish bin in a nearby park, threw it in, threw in several matches. This was wholly irresponsible of me, as that law-abiding citizen (once also taken at the tailor's against my better judgment) but in those few terrible hours, where was civilisation, where was rationality?

I stood beside the burning mass, till the fire engine arrived. The very nice fire men hosed out the fire, my once beautiful, virginal bedding a soggy, blackened, smouldering mess. And someone produced that cup of tea – do they carry a thermos of tea on every fire tender? There, there… I was patted (not dabbed – no Gerald there then) and comforted. But told, whilst I was a good citizen, not to try to put fires out myself in future.

That night I slept on the sofa, scene of, well, I could not think of such scenes then. The next day, I changed the locks. I gave the curtain to a tramp in the street who, surprised at its quality, was most grateful for the surrounding warmth of its folds. I changed the phone number. I fortified myself against the Wendon-Davis's. I felt more than invaded. You might have thought I was pre-occupied with... why he had chosen to bring that girl here? But I also wondered, how had she, Mrs W-D (I could not think of her as Phyllis), got my number?

I bought more bedding. Initially I had been tempted to set fire to the bed. Not to commit suttee on it, after all, my husband had not died. Gerald, another woman's husband, had only slept with yet another woman in it. Only.

After a long time, a thousand, thousand seconds in the cold hours of the night, that moment before dawn when life misses a heartbeat, the still at midday before the afternoon commences, rationality began to set in. A bed on fire two floors up in a building would present more practical problems than a bin in a park. Or a fire in the broken nuclear wastes of the heart.

16

Picking up the Pieces

About a week later the letter came. My name, no endearment, lots of swirls in that black ink.

> *I understand that I may have utterly unwittingly done something to offend you. If that is the case, it was of course totally unintentional and I apologise unreservedly. I hope whatever I did was not hurtful or offensive, or had any lasting impact. I am saddened that you did not feel we were good enough friends that you would be able to talk to me about the problem face to face. Then I could at least apologise in person but if that is your decision then I must abide by it.*

Ouch. Now you might draw breath in. You might say, what a cheek. What a load of hog's swill. You might well ask, is the writer talking about the same incident? Could it be possible Mrs W-D had stood over him and asked, for what was he was apologising for? Which would then account for such nonsense? What a ridiculous excuse!

It is true that a sensible person would not have opened the letter in the first place, they would have taken it to the terrace, burned it like the bedding, hardened their heart, pulled up the drawbridge. As an unseen observer that day, you might have looked through my tiny kitchen window, you might have seen me, picking up the silver letter-opener Gerald had given me for my last birthday (another weapon in hindsight I could have used against him), turning the cream watermarked envelope over in my hands. You, as the untrained eye, might have looked and seen me, apparently wistful for Gerald, lonely for Gerald, humiliated, trodden on, abused, foolish enough to open the letter.

In opening it, using the letter opener (*Only the masses rip the envelope, Sweeting*), there was a whiff of that scent, did that not remind me, not sicken me? True, it was unsullied with another's, the scent was as pure as Tony had made it, the lavender well to the top of the scent. Did you, the unseen observer, see me read it for what it was concreting over, not for what it was? The nuclear furnace, being covered by time, by need, by absence. Gerald wanted to apologise, wanted to come back. Never mind the ridiculousness of it. 'Unwittingly', 'unintentional', 'lasting impact'. Did I read these? Did they register? How stupid could I be? By then this was the lower courses of the river of what a cynic would scoffingly call our affair, of course there was rubbish in the flow, there was silt, emotional baggage, rocks, boulders. The channels of clear flow, of free thinking, were long since clogged. But there were still those last shrinking vestiges of love. To you, my observer, I clung to this apology, this apology of an apology, as though I was a drowning person clinging to a log in the inexorable flow of the water.

Or was I the black widow spider who after loving, kills her lover? Except of course, that the position was, technically, spoken for by Mrs W-D. No matter. Was it then – it must have been – that I began to spin my web? Accumulate the poison, plan the murder? Did I lie back on my bed – where he had lain with yet another of all the women he had lain with down the years – did I consciously conspire? Was it a daydream that, with repetition, became reality?

Flowers began to arrive. Every day. A long time ago when the world was still new, and I was not even a blot on the horizon, had Mrs W-D had them too? Is this how she had managed? Should I send mine to her? Presumably it was Wendy, she the long-suffering, presumably all-knowing, secretary at Wendon-Davis Associates, who arranged the flowers. Specially chosen. The first were pink everlasting sweet peas. Nothing extraordinary in that, beautifully scented, for obvious reasons. I put them on a vase in the kitchen table. My mother, who is now long past the pain her daughter took for so many years, told me these represent lasting pleasure. Hmm. Very funny. The next day, another lot of flowers were delivered. Completely out of season, these were a beautiful bunch of blue violets. (Mother: *Faithfulness*. My mother had one of those lists of flowers and what they signify, that now you only see in posh bookshops and occasionally on coffee tables, meaning that no one actually reads them.) Well, lovely as they were, and whatever they represented, you cannot avoid loving them. Then came another lot of the everlasting sweet peas. After that, lily of the valley (Mother: *Return of happiness*). And so on, through 'y' (yellow flowers, all different but the same colour) through to 'n' (again out of season, narcissus. And I knew what that meant without Mother's book having to tell me). Very clever. Crass, soppy, the thing young lovers do and everyone says 'ah'. My name in flowers. Tenuous connections to the initials in my name, but quite clever. With all the connotations of the flowers' meanings. Evelyn. A name Gerald never called me but via Wendy's orchestrations with the florist, he was acknowledging he had overstepped the mark and that I should be treated in an adult way. For a change. You might not see this, but remember, I had known this man for a very long time and I could hear him ticking. Like a bomb.

The flat (I have said it was small), began to resemble a funeral parlour, all the flowers, all the scents. There was no ticket with any of the flowers, nothing else to say who they were from but I knew the florist of old. Remember too, how many bouquets I have had pressed against me over the years. And always when Gerald knew (but never normally admitted) that he had sinned. This time, Gerald presumably thought his use and choice of flowers (or did Wendy supervise the actual choice, telling me, via the narcissus, what she thought of her boss?) would suffice for me to take him back, forgive him. *Why not?* his mind would tick, *she has always done it before.* With all the others.

Setting aside all the others, setting aside the location he had chosen, the invasion of my home, the massacre of my heart, the funny thing was that I could not forgive Gerald that Phyllis, Mrs Wendon-Davis, had rung me, at home and – even after all his thoughtlessness, the very crassness of his actions, the complete humiliation I had suffered, the whole appalling-ness of it all – the worst thing was that I had lied to her, to save him. What kind of peculiar, unwarranted, one-sided loyalty did this man seem to command? Was I mad?

Was I near to the end of the hundred-year sleep, begun so long ago, and just coming towards being wakened? And why, since I can see both sides of this ridiculous conundrum, why blame him for my own faithfulness? Perhaps I had too great a share of it, to compensate for his complete lack. True, I had slept with her husband, that was one thing, to steal him from her, but to lie to her? For him? It seemed appalling. It was the highest tide mark of immorality. I had sullied my good name by lying to her for him.

Ridiculous now, looking back, that I worried about lying to her, not sleeping with her husband. But there it was. Even thieves have their definition of honour.

17

The Table of Ceasefire

After such an incident, after inflicting such terrible pain, you might of course think that was the end of it all. Gerald was not such a person. He was, after all, the God of Connection. Clearly, he thought (insanely, you might think) that the letter was greater than the sum of its parts. My mother would have said here that presumably he too thought it made sense, but I never told her about the incident; indeed, I have never told of it before to anyone before I wrote it here. And the flowers, Gerald's way of seeking to make amends, after a while I suppose he thought they worked their magic. He would figure, I had forgiven him before, so why not now?

I cannot pretend that my heart did not jump at the very sight of him, a final flurry amid the swamps and marshes of the mature river that was our relationship, before reaching the sea. Of course he was still handsome, albeit going fast to seed. This day I was hurrying through Shepherd Market in the West End, full of those tiny but crammed grocery shops run by Arabs and Turks, full of fascinating goodies, juxtaposed cheek by jowl with art galleries, all white walls and wooden floors, the art with huge price tags packed into small rooms, the smell of coffee pervading everything, then all the sandwich bars, the street-café culture London now has, men in suits breakfasting or later in the day lunching outside with bottles of wine, almost European but not quite. Do not dwell on the former use of this market, once where ladies of the night successfully plied their trade.

Our eyes met, and I remember as I saw him, so he saw me. I saw his eyes widen. The traffic noise around us subsided. The rest of the world fell away. There was a silence, like people recovering themselves in the seconds after an explosion. Funny to think he could still have that effect of stopping the world. There was no one with him. He was sitting at a café table, drinking coffee. It was unseasonably warm for November that year, mid-November 2002. He had some papers with him. And there was the ubiquitous black-inked pen.

I did not stop to wonder why he was there, or to think how close we were to Curzon Street and those infamous mews, where presumably they still talk of the night the pizzas kept coming. No, the shock of him, the very physical sight of him took all of that from my mind. Did the conductor have something musically light and airy to accompany this delectation? Did I hear him tap his baton, to muster the orchestra? All my plans for the morning turned to mist and evaporated. The day was young, the air clear. Isn't it strange now, how often I have written this, that on the very sight of him, my whole world turned and turned about?

Having locked eyes, the world having steadied after the jolt of the shock of recognition, I was almost hypnotised. The moth and the flame. He smiled, putting down the pen, and began to rise in welcome. And I, suddenly oblivious to my surroundings, smiled back. I was an automaton. It was like first meeting again. I almost heard the violins, but then the musicians looked again and thought better of it.

After years of attrition, two combatants briefly recall together what it was like before the war began. The peace talk, after all the flag-waving of the flowers, began. I completely forgot whatever I had been going to do, where I had been going. Gerald had that effect. My smile was already widening. Despite all that had happened, a huge balloon of happiness welled up inside.

I found myself leaning forward to receive his kiss. On the cheek, both cheeks. And we drew back, still in each other's aura, holding each other, and smiled. That special smile between old lovers. I could smell the crushed lavender. Funnily enough it did not make me feel sick. Perhaps I had been anaesthetised. Within the ambit of that familiar scent there had already been a lifetime of forgiving. Perhaps that was how I was there at all. I could see the dark-grey of his eyes, the crinkling of his crow's feet, the mole beside his eye riding the creases of skin, the sheer joy in his face. He really was pleased, delighted even, to see me.

"Hello," he said, no pretence at the dark chocolate 'pulling' voice. Just a smiling tone, surprised, happy. We hugged each other, a great big unashamed hug. My arms seemed to go round him more easily than I remembered. "What a nice surprise, a pleasure," he said. "Come and have a coffee with me." And reaching to hold my hand, with the other he moved the papers, pulled back a chair for me and, as I sat, into the curve of his arm onto the seat, of course the waiter was there, the order given. Same old Gerald, why should anything change just because my world had been rocked on its axis? But it was only afterwards I thought that.

There was no point in going over the incident, in reality only four weeks or so previously. Though probably the worst of its kind, it was, after all, only one of many over the years. If you sup with the Devil then sometimes you will have indigestion. I have said that mistresses rant, but by then, there was no point. I was sitting there, he was sitting there. We had kissed, like civilised people; it was a kind of temporary ceasefire. How funny to use such words about love.

"Sweeting, my lovely," he said, letting out a huge breath, taking my hand in his. "I have missed you." And turning that hand over, looking at it as though he could read my palm, he went on. "What have we done to deserve each other? Are you going to follow me so we can torture each other through Eternity?" And then something, well something I have waited a lifetime for, he smiled his most charming, most handsome smile, his grey eyes all a-crinkle: "Of them all, you know, I have loved you the most." Did my heart expand with happiness, did I really take in breath? Too late. Why is it only now I might think of Gerald at his most artful? With fences to build?

I thought little of this at the time but looking back this was unusual, Gerald looking inwards. And the reference to death. Gerald had always had it that he was immortal, not going to die. Perhaps he recognised how far he had gone. Or had someone just turned him down? Highlighted their difference in age? Was I truly becoming a kind of Madame de Pompadour he would return to for comfort, solace, but nothing sexual? And after so long?

Disregarding the actual meaning of the question, on we went, we laughed, our hands beginning to dance, our fingers fluttering. In a ceasefire discussion, despite the pleasantries, each side is aware of the transitory nature of the exchange. A little later in the day, he gathered his papers (actually it was the crossword, he had the previously hidden paper folded in four, having presumably read the rest. Things were going well on the clue-solving front, judging from the black ink all over the black-and-white square), capped the pen, paid the bill, then we strolled along the street and lunched together. Not a propelling across the restaurant lunch, I had had too many of those and, besides, Gerald had had no time, or apparently felt the inclination to make the arrangements that had otherwise preceded his arrival, impressed so many women, including, a long, long time ago, a younger and more foolish me. That day Gerald had oysters (why does my mind trick me into remembering this?), a dozen, washed down with Guinness and champagne. See, I cannot recall what I ate. Was my whole life so totally subsumed into his?

There was one thing I had to ask. How had Mrs W-D got my number? It was virtually the only reference to that day. There was no verbal apology, Gerald's pen and the flowers were supposed to have covered that.

"Oh," said Gerald, best airy hand gesture to the fore, "I had doodled it on a pad and, when she asked, I told her you were writing a book. And I am helping you," he paused, bringing his face near mine, lowering his voice, "between the sheets, so to speak." He smiled his big Photo-Me smile and flicked up his eyebrow. A Gerald joke. One close to the bone. The planes of his face shifted and crimped slightly over the scar from a mugging, years before. I did not mention the conflagration of the sheets. To be silent is not to forget. Those sitting temporarily at the table of ceasefire do not dwell on previous atrocities. Privately, they add them up, seeking vengeance for them when the other party is not looking.

Once upon a time, my heart might have leapt – like a salmon coursing up, out and against the tide of the stream – at the idea he had thought of me and doodled round my number, like a schoolboy carving my initials into his desk. But not now. Just think, once, many, many moons ago, he had come to me, looking very uncomfortable and I had jumped up with pleasure at the sight of him. "Steady, Sweeting," he had said, as I had run to his arms. "No coupling, not just now. Got a touch of the unmentionables. Must hold back." It turned out to be crabs. Of course, I would not learn, would not steady (was I that racehorse of the day in Mr George's curtains again?). We came together and later that week I went to the doctor with my own crabs. Imagine how embarrassing it was, to pick an insect off yourself, your most intimate area, and see its arms waving up at you. The shame of it. Remember the story about the leopard – you cannot change its spots. What we do for love. But think for a moment, what would I have done if it had been AIDS? Diced with death just for the very pleasure of having Gerald in my arms, in my bed? Experience is a hard school and I, the fool, had learned in no other.

Nevertheless, this day we talked like old friends, like the long old lovers we were, who have searched every corner of each other's being, touched every part of each other's body, dragged down the other's soul, risen with them to the heights. We lingered over coffee, dallied over paying the bill. Reluctant to part, having managed the no man's land between our camps, we picked up each conversation, our eyes encouraging each other to keep talking, to have the excuse to be together, keep the rest of the world on hold. In the gently lengthening shadows of that unseasonably warm November afternoon, Time stood gently by, waiting for us to catch up.

Of course, despite all my doubts, in spite of what had happened, toward evening, which comes early at that time of year, we ended up in bed, I dancing on his fingers, he urging me, "Just another, just one more, Sweeting," each time I reached a crescendo. "Dance on the light of the moon, the moon," he whispered, urging me on. "Dance on the light of the moon," as if each orgasm was an achievement, was his orgasm. Like a couple who have danced together for a lifetime, we knew the steps, hardly needing the beat of the music, to sway and sashay, our bodies bound together in the oldest rhythm in the world. Was he trying at long last, to make up for all those other times and all those other women? I did not ask then. We were wrapped in each other's pleasure, just for that one afternoon. Like that last month before the outbreak of the First World War, how golden and precious it seemed then.

Between us was an affectionate warmth, like late afternoon sunshine at the end of August, golden, lingering, weakening after the zenith of high summer. Shortly, the season would begin the change, acknowledging the mellowness that stole over us that afternoon. Next day, Gerald sent flowers – chrysanthemums, harbinger of autumn – as thanks for that gentle, late, unseasonably warm afternoon, before what was sown in spring, ripened during the summer, shall be gathered in. Before the harshness of winter comes.

18

The Act

And so war was rejoined. Or not war, the affair, the dance. But not quite in the same way. We had crossed the Rubicon. Older, weary of the exchange, tired, the combatants slug away at each other. Why, you might ask? Habit? Convenience? The rut of love? Were we canalised then that however the flow of water tried, we could not break out? Were we really committed irrevocably in that course?

Now, murdering someone you love is actually quite difficult. The specific pleasure of them has to be put to one side, when you are thinking of such a course of action. In fact, in the end – no pun intended – it is immaterial whether you love them or not. I spent a lot of time thinking about it. Should I buy a big chest freezer and somehow, one night with the moon in the right quarter and the wind from the east, manage to pitch a very large and strong Gerald in? What does it take to kill a man? Would I have to stun him first? Would I be able to shut the door on him? All of him? Or think of this idea – Gerald and I sailing on a yacht. Not the *Geraldine*, another, a smaller one. What little I know of sailing comes from *Swallows and Amazons*, but just think, when the yacht comes about, and Gerald cracks his head on the beam of the jib. Would that be enough to kill him, to knock him into the sea? But thinking on it further, and knowing Gerald, he would probably come up swimming with dolphins. After a lifetime of it, indeed dogged by it, I could see the headlines: *MP's husband rescued by dolphins.* This would not do.

You can hardly apply to the local college for evening classes in 'the best way to commit murder' or 'the cleanest way to leave the scene'. Tablets? Passé, darling, been there, done it. And I could not go into the pub and ask the best route to shoot someone in the public eye (or so he liked to think and very often was but not always for the right reasons). Or not the pubs I frequented. And you could hardly make a public announcement either there or in the small ads.

It would not be possible to ring the AA and ask ever-so-sweetly: *Which cables under the bonnet do I cut to greatest effect?* And if I found an evening class in motor mechanics, would it not seem strange that I was only interested in stopping the car in the most dangerous way possible? You know the sort of question: *Which is the brake wire and what is the best thing to cut it with?* You just know too, that, all supposing the opportunity arose, if I found Gerald's car in a dark and unattended place, and I went under the bonnet, the God of All-seeing Reason, as opposed to He of the Quiet Satisfactions, would ensure that I would only cut what I thought were brake wires. I could just imagine it. Gerald would turn up late, I would look surprised. Surprised? I would be shocked at the sight of him, the words *How did you escape?* throttling me in the effort to force them back down my throat. And he would wave his arm and say something like, *Came by taxi, Sweeting, something wrong with the wife's motor.* Or worse, just think, supposing I did all the right things, went to the evening class, or learned the position of the brakes – weren't they the same in all cars? – and, the God of Unintended Consequences at work here, I killed her. Mrs W-D. Phyllis. No, I never thought of her as Phyllis. Mrs Wendon-Davis. I had nothing against her. Imagine meeting her in Heaven one day, a rueful expression on my face. *Sorry,* I would have to say, *I didn't mean it.* Is all that fair in love and other women's husbands? Would she understand?

And if Gerald suspected, would he turn up with a huge bouquet of flowers? The wreath for the death I had not managed to orchestrate. What would he know? What would he suspect? With hindsight, would he say how sorry he was I missed?

There was one night a few years ago now that a tapping on the door woke me. A persistent tapping. It could not be Gerald, he had his own key. He had after all provided the wherewithal to pay for the flat, a key was the least I could have given him. (And look, my mother would say, if she had known, what he gave to you.) And if Gerald, for whatever reason, was key-less, well, he would have thundered on the door, crying out to be let in. *Come on, Sweeting,* he would cry. *Break open a glass of something and make a thirsty soul sing.* Or something like that. The time of night was irrelevant. Gerald wanted to come in so he would let everyone know. So I knew the tapping was not him.

I opened the door. It was Gerald, about to begin to tap again. But not at normal door height; he was slumped down near the bottom of the door. I began to say the usual, like *What are you doing down there?* when I actually looked at him properly and realised there was a lot of blood. Now from little wounds, there is much more blood generated than is necessary, presumably in inverse proportion to make you run around and fuss, but with a big wound (and I am now arguably something of an expert), in my experience, there is hardly any. And Gerald had two wonderful black eyes. Something unpleasant had also opened his nose, a big gash, across the brow.

Gerald had been mugged. Or so he mumbled then. And the later gossip page reported the same from a press release issued by Wendy for Wendon-Davis Associates. It was true that he had been beaten up. Very comprehensively. His face had taken a particular battering, there had to be stitches in the fine skin, the planes temporarily spoilt and then always after faintly scarred. His glasses had been broken in the fray. The planes of his face ever after were always slightly interrupted across previously smooth cheeks. In fact it was not true to say he had been mugged. Another woman. I knew there were other women – how could I not know? But there was a man involved too, Gerald had touched another woman and offended another man. Who mugs a man, leaves the wallet, the cards, the cufflinks and the watch? Takes nothing, not the very well-stocked wallet of connections and money, the expensive jewellery? But leaves an impressive calling card of bruises and cuts. Gerald muttered something about being caught in an alleyway. Where presumably he had been set upon. I went with him to the hospital where they treated him solicitously and swiftly, even as smashed up as he was, recognising Mr Wendon-Davis and not really wanting him underfoot, so to speak. Fortunately it was not a Saturday night or we might have been squeezed in between an overdrugged teenager to be stomach pumped once the hallucinations stopped or the victims of a road accident, awaiting transfusions of blood. When finally he came back with me to the flat, to my bed, and I held him against me to the warmth of my body, till he was an utter, utter sleeping weight, should I have unstitched the stitches, rubbed salt into the wounds so they scarred? It might not have killed him but it would have remade a trifle of his now-mended face. A used and spoilt trifle, the untidy remains of a beautiful dessert. The other man clearly had wanted to ruffle Gerald's smooth, if gently aging but pampered, beauty. And I could do nothing to affect the twinkle in his eye, short of blinding him, which was unthinkable. I loved his eyes; despite all they chose to survey, I loved their twinkle.

And I know it was another woman because when I helped him up from the slumped position on my step (how had he got up the stairs?), before I took him in my arms, I could smell her. Presumably Gerald had done more than touch her. The lavender was tainted with musk. God alone knew what her man – or the one who had taken it upon himself to wreak revenge or warning on Gerald – had done to her, after he had seen to Gerald.

In the end it was quite simple really. It was a while after the conflagration in the park. Do they say that time heals wounds? Did the passage of time really make what happened easier? Indeed, even with what I know now, I am surprised still that it was so simple.

It was a Sunday in December, the days short, the sun low in the sky, the air cold and colder still by the sea. We often stayed by the sea, Gerald loved to hear the motion of the water, even through the night. It was that time of year where you value every minute of sunshine, daylight itself being also in such short supply. The light was still bright though, crystal sharp, making your eyes hurt despite the brief daylight. No wonder artists migrate to the coast to paint; everything becomes so distinct, so utterly absolute in such light. There were no artists working that day though. The wind was bitter, taking no prisoners in its icy blasts. People rushed out, walked the dog, got the papers, rushed back to the fire, the sherry and the next meal. We had a weekend by the coast, in one of those innumerable cottages Gerald had access to, through 'friends', along the Suffolk coast. Other Gerald types, all interconnecting. This cottage was at Aldeburgh, right in amongst the tiny Alice in Wonderland icing cake houses there, *so terribly English seaside*, as per Gerald, signifying in some way his view that the English play at being by the sea, indulge all their childhood fantasies in the construction of the buildings there. The houses are a mad juxtaposition of styles, hotchpotch Dutch gables, dainty icing cake designs, all the colours of the rainbow, all of it facing bravely but madly up to the ravages of the North Sea, the wind and the tides. It is the kind of place where people drink sherry before Sunday lunch, except that, at that time of year, most of the Boden-clad mannequins who can be seen gracing the place in August, were drinking sherry in other parts of the country, mostly, I suspect, London.

In winter all the houses on the seafront reveal themselves to be summer residences, mostly rented out. You can tell that from the bare windows and double doors opening on to the beach path, where people have not troubled to curtain them because the nights are long in summer and, with luck, warm. The furniture is all wicker, and the tables are long and covered in plastic tablecloths. Bicycles are kept in the main room. By night, the rooms are not lit. In winter daylight, you notice that there are a lot of books in Aldeburgh, shelves and windows lined with them. Other than eating and drinking, once night falls, there is the cinema, manned by volunteers, but not much else to do in Aldeburgh. So clearly, people sit out on their terraces, in their summer chairs and read. But in November and December, it is the builders' terrain – there is much knocking and banging as repairs are made before the worst of the winter weather strikes. The town becomes more private, perhaps more intimate. "It is the perfect place," so Gerald would declare with a wink and gusto "to have an affair!" and he would reach for me. We would tumble into the sheets, laughing.

The cottage we had that weekend is by the beach, with a view of the sea from the kitchen window, very grey, full of white horses, racing before the wind. Often I should imagine the windows must be broken, where they face the beach, if the tide picks up the pebbles and dashes them against the glass. Perhaps the cottage was too far back from the wave action. It was a wonderful place for the weekend, the place empty and unseasonal but very lovely just the same. We had stayed there several times, hence I knew about the builders. Well, I should correct this, by saying that I was there for the weekend; Gerald was doing his usual top-and-tail act to the weekend, appearing one day, coming back either the next or the day after that, after duties at High Fold. Or in grammatical terms, a capital letter at the beginning and a full stop at the end. It was to be a full stop.

There was such a chill wind coming off the sea, I had decided to cook a roast. When I was a child, my mother used to cook roast on Sundays, to have cold on Mondays. People don't seem to do this anymore. And an apple crumble. I love the smell of apple crumble cooking. And Gerald appreciated it. I saw the car arrive; by this time, it was a dark-blue Jag. He came down the alley between the cottages, the buildings all cheek by jowl with each other, his arms full of flowers, and chocolates and champagne. I could hear him singing. Was it…? Well, I could not guess at the song, he hummed so many things and so badly. Then there he was in the doorway, a big man, a handsome and elegant man, blocking the whole frame, making the room suddenly smaller, full. Perfectly attired as always, but he still glanced in the mirror. Assessment: Good, maybe Good to Perfect. I could see it in his eyes. It was rather like the shipping forecast: …Dogger Bank, Moderate becoming Good… Channel Light Vessel Automatic, Good becoming Moderate… Fastnet, Moderate becoming Good… Wendon-Davis, Good to Perfect.

He was early leaving High Fold; I was not really expecting him till later. But no matter, there he was, full of smiles, full of hugs, the scent of crushed flowers, lilies I think, his lavender, full of life.

"Hello, my lovely, and how are you? A sight for sore eyes indeed," he said, all crinkled nose, all laughter lines. How could you do anything but smile, your spirits beginning to dance, raise your face for his kiss, rub yourself against him, like a cat? His skin tasted of salt, salt from the sea air. He must have stood outside for a moment, looking at the waves, taking it all in. And now there he was, all smiles, all mine for the afternoon. Lunch seemed quite different suddenly. That was Gerald, the sheer pleasure of him. The joy of the man.

Coming in further, he sniffed the air appreciatively, like a hound sniffing the early morning scent, waiting for the hunt to commence.

"Lovely smell, Sweeting, is there a little something for me?" He came and busied himself in the kitchen; well, that is, he took up all the room in the kitchen, which was tiny. Clearly these weekend types do not spend long communally cooking. There just was not room. Perhaps they just bring a huge casserole and reheat it. He opened the champagne, which of course would have been chilled by the weather, but, knowing Gerald, would be chilled anyway. He had one of those fancy compartments for just such things in his car. As Gerald Wendon-Davis would do. Wendy must have included it specially in the spec for the car. We drank it, fizzing, chilled, before lunch. "Here's mud in your eye," raising our glasses before settling companionably over the Sunday papers. They were, as Gerald liked to put it, 'fully loaded', full of gossip and intrigue. Gerald was terribly happy. I was happy. It was all so cosy. Our feet entwined as we read; it was a very small room.

Lovely Gerald, of course he was. How can I think otherwise? Whatever had happened, painfully, amazingly, I was still in love. He was such a… well, such a vibrant life, such a fun person. He could still take my breath away, just the sight of him. That day he was so very happy. I think it was one of Gerald's days of 'good copy' as he had several stories in good positions. It was one of those days you can hear the music playing though the radio is silent. There were smiles on our faces, taps to our toes. We finished the champagne before the carving that prefaces, indeed heralds, a good roast lunch.

Now, after a crime, it is recognised that every witness bears a different story of what happened. The mind plays mysterious tricks on people, so that if there has been a gun involved, one person will say there were four gunshots whilst another will say there was only two or perhaps three. Think of the Kennedy assassination and how many shots were supposed to have been aimed over the grassy knoll, from how many different directions. In this instance, it is hard to put two stories together as one of the protagonists is no longer capable of speaking the same language as the one who remains.

What was it that changed? The sun coming out suddenly, the bright light in the window, did it blind me? Or was something going wrong with lunch, was the gravy spoiling? Did it exasperate me, so that I was not careful where I waved the knife? Perhaps I was tired of it all, perhaps he was; perhaps it was time. Another week ahead, another week of not quite knowing, where would he be, who would he be with? That time and tide in the affairs of a man and a woman, which taken at the flood, leads to murder. Or suicide? Who knows?

It is possible that I was so suddenly enraged at the sight of him that when I found the carving knife in my hand, all the humiliation, debasement, abuse came back. Gone, in the blink of an eye, went all the memories of fun, laughter, ridiculous stances, daft comments made between lovers. You could think that the smell of lavender drove me back to that terrible scene in my flat, my home, my castle against the world, which he had invaded for one careless, carefree afternoon of sex. Yes, spit the word out, sex. Was that it, the straw that broke the camel's back? After all those years with all those other women? Stab I went (you could say), shoving the knife in hard. Is that what happened?

I could say I was serving lunch, having taken the meat out, the oven gloves still on my hands and he walked on to the knife. Just like that. Or a court might say, in long-winded legalese, that I stabbed him. Put another way, I could say I was about to offer the carving knife to him and, being closer than I had anticipated, the sun in my eyes, the glare flashing off the blade in my hand, he turned, and stabbed himself, impaled himself on it. And there he was, the Collector, finally pinned, rather than doing the pinning.

And if I turned these stories around, so that you came to them in a different order, would you feel differently about them? What words could I use to change your view? 'What if…?' Is this not the saddest combination of words in the English language? On a par perhaps with the longing of 'If only…' Such a short phrase but summarising the rosy haze of so much wistful regret, such pain brought only with experience. Or plain tinkering with the truth, misting over the facts, smudging the ink on the page.

What is true is this. It was all so fast, so quick. If I changed them around would the last version linger in your mind longest? But then death is death – once there, how much does the *modus operandi* of how you got there actually matter?

Ridiculously – in that way your mind can dream up a theory of nuclear physics in the twinkling of an eye, solve the world's hunger, reach for the stars in poetry, all so easy, so fast, so cunning, you cannot believe it was only a matter of seconds – I thought of carving chicken. There was a point of resistance on the blade, then in it went, almost like a sigh, the skin giving way. Into my mind came the memory of Gerald's white skin. Just like chicken.

Did he turn on the knife? And when does shock turn to intent? My shock. His intent. Or my intent and his accepting shock? He moved forward, I moved back, the knife between us, linking us, in him. At my most cynical, you could even say, as in life so in death, Gerald facilitated the connection. But it was all so quick, the taking of a life, the leaving of a life. Is that the way he wanted it?

Gerald with a knife in him. It sounds so silly to write it down. I glanced at his face. There was a look of surprise between us. Ridiculously (well it was all ridiculous), I thought it must hurt. "Look what has happened to me," he said, just like an opera singer, making a huge fuss of the stab, not like I had done it at all. Opera singers take so long to die. They make such a thing of it, arias and arias taken up with 'She stabbed me, she stabbed me', as they stagger about the stage, gasping their death throes at such length. Now he did not seem so surprised. Such a simple thing and now so final. Did I hear the cheers from all those masses of women, taken in by the champagne and the unseasonal fruits? Or was there a whisper in the air, a faint release of the words, *at last*?

This was Gerald centre stage for the last time. "Look," he whispered as he came to his knees, a huge hulk of a man crumpling, putting his hand to the knife. Taking the spotlight, alone on the stage. Filling most of the kitchen floor. And like they do in films, so he graciously fell back, so that I could, in turn, kneel to him, see his eyes close, as though he was resting, and hear the sigh – like they say in films there is one, the last sigh of breath easing out of him – still holding the knife. Always the dramatic interlude, the dramatic finish. It was all so quick. No last loving words then. The 'Moonlight Sonata', there it was in my head, recalled from our night under the Spanish Steps in Rome, that evening promised so much and created so much pain; Beethoven's wooing of the moon; this time the piano's final notes dropped away. It was the end of the piece. And the pianist bowed his head, closed the piano and quietly left the stage. On his way out, I heard the door close. There was complete silence.

Gerald lay back, one hand almost to his head. Very theatre, very Hollywood in the thirties. People don't die like they used to. Life ebbs out of people in books. But normally in books there is a death rattle, but the only rattling was the water in the pipes, gurgling, full of life, still moving, still responding. One could no longer say that of Mr W-D.

19

The Finale

The story should really end there. I should have been arrested. Certainly, I waited for the knock at the door. But there was a bit more.

Mrs W-D, as well connected apparently or better than her husband, wove a web better than I could have even guessed at. The professional Black Widow but then it was her legal role. I had just performed the deed. Or facilitated it. You could say I had saved her the job. But there was no whiff of scandal. It is not relevant to this story what happened next, how I removed the oven gloves I had worn, took the lunch, stepping over Gerald, threw the lunch away, left Gerald there, gathering the chill to his body as the finality and ritual of death completed its formalities. The oven gloves I burned, though why I was anxious to cover such evidence when there was so much else, I don't know. How strange that one worries about clearing up at such times. If you want to know, it was the number plate that found him out, the police checked it when he did not appear in London at the appointed time. I wonder if when given the information about the number plate, the policeman was tempted to say *Oh GAWD* but then probably he sees such things all the time. By then, Gerald must have been meeting his God in person. But all of that is apart from this story. Mrs W-D took over where I had left off. The next act. As though written.

I went back to London. And waited, expectantly. Sadly. The papers said that Gerald died of a single self-induced stab wound, depressed following a long fight (it is always a battle) with cancer. Have you ever heard such rubbish? No mention of me at all. I thought I had had a starring role. Only eighteen hours or so before. I killed him. Did I? If you wave a knife about and someone walks on to it, that's murder, or manslaughter at the very least. But no, even that was taken from me. Mrs W-D knew her stuff. Of the two of them, she and Gerald, she proved the better connector; she pulled the strings, she covered up. Second rule of Gerald: *only use the good or the bad publicity, cover the truly awful.* She had learned well. Perhaps she had taught him.

And there was a note. The papers said he left a note. A note? Can you write a note when someone kills you? Stop the downward gesture, the fast left or right thrust, the shotgun bullet and say 'wait a minute, I need to write a note'? How ridiculous. It was a set-up. A lie. What of this then? The note apparently began:

I understand that I may have done something to offend you. I could not help myself any longer...

That's not a suicide note. It was taken from the bin. There it was, in one of the Sundays, described as all crumpled. I knew the note, knew it for what it really was. It was one of the initial drafts for that ridiculous note he had written to me, after that night, that distasteful incident, one of so, so many. She had known her man all right, had known the content of his wastepaper bins. All that conniving and secrecy for nothing. He had left the evidence about and she had gathered it. For just such occasions. A book on Suffolk churches! Hah! God knows what dirt she must have had on him, down the years.

And cancer? Gerald? But of course, if true of course he must have known. And not told me. Was it true? He had told no one. Dammit, I had done him a favour. He robbed me even then. It was not the revenge I was seeking, for years of abasement. Dammit, I murdered him when he was too cowardly to commit suicide. Gerald, you cheated on me, even in death.

I was robbed too in the manner of his death. There was no knock at the door, no burly policeman reading me my rights (ridiculously I wonder, what do thin policemen do at such times?). Eventually I could only surmise that it was Gerald's hand finally on the knife; he was bigger than me, his hand apparently took my prints off it. Think of it, he had taken my prints, he had held the knife. Or Mrs W-D's connections did. Even in death, scandal was tempered, not allowed. No accidents. The police never even rang me. I had even been robbed of my sweetest moment: revenge. By him. By his wife. The wife is mightier than the mistress. The pen beat the sword. The artistry of the pen outlasts the swipe of the sword, no matter how deep the cut. What could I do? I could hardly write to my MP.

There was something else too. Looking back, I have described what happened in such a bloodless fashion, but nothing can ever prepare you for the shock, the aftershock and the regret, the memory of actually holding on to a knife as it pierces living flesh. It is hardly like carving a chicken, never mind whatever ridiculous thought had come into my mind at the time. The chicken is a dead bird, cooked and not someone you are in love with. Albeit that that person has a knife embedded in them. And the shocking realisation – as though an electric current – that you've done something so utterly basic, apparently casting aside the whole veneer of civilisation, social mores, training, breaching a fundamental rule of society, that you have actually felt a knife in someone living, never mind how it got there or what your relationship to the impaled person is. And again, my MP would not have been the person to talk it over with. And Gerald, well, self-evidently Gerald was not there anymore.

Gerald died with remarkably few headlines, only those along the lines of *Husband for Member for Norfolk North East takes life*, little mention of any apparent depression and the cancer. Where was *Lover gets revenge*, or *Lover stabs husband for Member in the Bright Green Suit*? What happened to the credit for all those diary stories? How fickle are the press? Gerald had sat at the Devil's dinner table even till the previous evening and the Devil had repaid him by completely forgetting Gerald had been there.

There were, however, many obituaries, some of which I suspect he had had a hand in. Certainly, some of them were very loquacious in a style with which I was long familiar. I saved them for the press-cutting book, the final chapter in print, marking his life in the public eye.

He was well remembered too at the funeral. I had a huge hat – well, truth to tell, most unusually there were lots of hats. It was difficult to see who was whom under the brims, which on reflection was presumably why so many women chose to wear them.

All those people I had known via long acquaintance with photographs were there. The family likeness across the generations was stamped across their faces as though it was shouted from the rooftops. No DNA tests required here to establish a connection. Gerald's two brothers, several nephews and nieces, yes and now-elegant Greg from that summer fete all those years ago, and that moment in the V&A Museum, of being passed over to protect him; then the time when we actually met, the secrets between us; there he was, broader of course, perhaps taller, very handsome in his mourning, a dark Nehru-style collar to the black silk jacket, so elegantly tailored to his shoulders and waist, perfect across the back. Had he made the suit? It was very beautiful, the edges of the collar delicately stretched into the hand-stitching at the neck. We nodded at each other, unspoken partners colluding with our secrets. I kept my third secret from him, my role in Gerald's death, or rather Mrs W-D had done it for me. I had brought them all together that day, with my actions, or rather my reaction to Gerald.

If I had not been numb with grief – yes, even I grieved after everything – I would have told some of them how proud Gerald was of their achievements. And he was, so terribly proud. Particularly of Greg's but I think, by then, even Greg must have had more than an inkling. Of the others, some of them, I knew everything about them, recounted in phone calls, letters (in between the Suffolk churches), numerous lunches, pillow talk, Gerald expanding on their successes and fallbacks, as well as on Greg's. Like the Kennedy families of this world, Wendon-Davises do not fail, they suffer a setback, from which to build upon. But it is the way of the mistress, to listen, to know, but not to be heard and never to be known. Not in public.

Amid all this thought, I was surprised at the choice of hymns. We sang, till the rafters rocked, 'I Vow to Thee My Country', which I am sure Gerald would have approved of, though probably not chosen. With considerable feeling I sang of the unquestioning love, the tested love, that gives the dearest and the best, that never falters (though maybe mine did), that pays the price, the love that makes, unfailingly, the final sacrifice. I knew about all of those things. Intimately. As presumably did Mrs W-D, though from another angle.

We also sang 'The Day Thou Gavest, Lord, Is Ended'. I was transported back to the country churches of my childhood, the tears pouring down my cheeks for times past. It is true that the past is another country; those who reach it do so by the visa of memory, which depletes with time. I cried, for Gerald's passing. That I had helped bring about. How had Mrs W-D covered it up?

And fancy that, you murder someone, or, at the very least, assist them en route, and you attend the funeral. No wonder in television programmes the police also attend, thinking themselves inconspicuous behind the gravestones. Inconspicuous! What nonsense. I know a burly policeman when I see one, gravestone or not. There were several. But looking at them properly, all of them were Gerald's connections, all grieving too that day. One stood up and read, almost as if Gerald had left a message, from Henry Scott Holland's *Death Is Nothing at All*. My face cupped in my hands, I only heard: "Laugh as we always laughed at the little jokes that we enjoyed together." There had been so many, a lot of them appalling. Then, the policeman read from the poem, for Gerald: "I am waiting for you, for an interval, somewhere very near, just round the corner. All is well. Nothing is hurt; nothing is lost. One brief moment and all will be as it was before." I did not hear the rest.

Even then, from beyond the grave, Gerald could surprise me. It seemed Gerald was born a Catholic but lapsed. I had known him all those years, all those long, funny, fanciful, splendid, painful years and I had never known. Not just catholic in his tastes but Catholic in his spiritual cups. Why had he never said? This was completely new to me, utterly uncharted territory.

I stood in that cold, scented church, a hand clutching my heart. What had I done to his soul, if he had not received last rites? Did the Catholic Church still do that? Would it still count if he had changed churches, for convenience? And if it was seen as suicide, what would St Peter say to him at the Pearly Gates? Would Gerald be forever assigned to remain outside Heaven? And if I had not known that, what else had I not been a party to, not let into the secret of? How had Mrs W-D got that past the party – sorry, the Party – as clearly she was not Catholic but dear old, all-embracing, totally comprehensive C of E? How would I explain that away, once I got to Heaven? All these questions, destined to remain unanswered now. In future, I could only surmise the responses. Gerald was no longer there to ask. I could hear his mocking expression, *Never complain, never explain*, fancying himself royalty. How ignorant of this man I had loved a lifetime I truly was.

Then there was Mrs Wendon-Davis herself, now a widow. I had taken from her what little she had had of

Gerald. Weekend duties, occasional appearances together. I did not think of the marital bed or whatever had happened in it. Was it separate rooms? Did she miss the lavender and cut grass, as I found I increasingly did? In spite of everything. And the seasons, who was there to tell me of the change in the seasons, the time of day, all those Gerald-isms? Would she miss this too?

She was in black, from head to toe, but no hat. There was, after all, no need to hide who she was. The hair a helmet, the lipstick resolute, the shoulders back. I have mocked her many times, but this day she was upright, apart from us all, very dignified. She looked older than the pictures from the House, the lines carved in her face. At one point, near the grave, by accident I found I was almost shoulder to shoulder with her, as she picked up the earth and threw it in. Did they do that in the Catholic Church, from dust we come, to dust we return? By then I was past listening, beyond reason, in the quiet desolation beyond despair. How was she managing?

Later, she was in a welcoming line of one, the other half of the reason why we were all there. I don't like the phrase 'the other half'. I know, as I drowned in grief, this was clutching at straws but he had been mine, sometimes. She and I shook hands. I looked into her blue eyes, steely blue eyes, and our hands clenched in the familiar gesture. We did not linger in the clasp. And she did not quite catch my name, and that day it did not matter. She had cleared up after me, after I had done the dirty work for her. I did not care to be reminded of the afternoon we had first and last spoken. Did I fancy a spark of recognition, or did that die away, covered, smothered even, as she had covered up what had happened?

A few days later the solicitor who had coughed over the flat to me, with Mrs W-D's money all those years before, rang and asked me to visit his offices. Somewhat surprised, I went. The offices are not in a well-known part of London. Nor are they particularly well appointed, as such offices go. Mr Frobisher was not exactly the family lawyer but someone Gerald used, had used for more vague if not nefarious activities. I was expecting nothing from Gerald, anticipating nothing. Lovers are not normally named in the will. Even those you have spent a lifetime with.

I sat in front of the solicitor's desk. He was very grey and, in comparison to the flame he had served, now six feet under, Mr Frobisher was rather drab. Unlike Gerald, he was one of those who 'do'. As I did finally for Gerald. In a way I had never truly anticipated. Now, Mr Frobisher opened a drawer and drew out an envelope. He coughed in that discreet way such persons do, bringing my attention back to his words. "About a year ago," he was saying, "Mr Wendon-Davis asked me to hold this. Until today. It is for you."

And so it was. There was my name, my Christian name, so rarely used, in between us, in Gerald's so-familiar script, all loops, loops, swirls and whorls. Saying nothing more, Mr Frobisher gave it to me. He shook my hand, a strange thing to do or so I thought, and left the room.

I turned it over. The last envelope. What was in it? My heart beating very loudly, there was no other sound. I opened it. The flap of the envelope was folded in; I did not need the blade of a letter opener. The weapon had already been used enough.

No lingering hint of lavender, cut grass, the envelope had been parted from Gerald for too long, kept for this day in the desk of the drab solicitor, the offices of Frobisher, Chapman and Dodd. There are not words sufficient in the English language to contain the sense of loss. Gerald had written this of Max; now I understand what he meant. Absurdly, I thought there would be no more "The dew is thickening on the field in the mornings, autumn is almost upon us," or "The crows are nesting higher in the trees – the summer will be hot," or unsought surveys of Suffolk churches. No more maddening moments, no more 'aperitifs', no more seasonal observations of 'our' life in which I had no part, no more loving, no more dancing in the dark, not needing to know the tune, no more white card invitations. No more. I had put a stop to all of those.

Inside the envelope, clearly from Gerald – I recognised the pattern under the flap – was one sheet of paper. I pulled it out. In the silence, I could hear a fly buzzing against a window, banging angrily on the capturing glass. I sat for a moment, holding the letter, just as it had come out of the envelope. There was a thundering in my ears. My heart was pounding on the inside of my ribs. In the fold of a letter, how many hopes are held, raised aloft, dashed asunder in the opening of the creases? Or carried with joy, lifted, lifted, lifting the spirit? Down the years think of what news a folded letter can carry, what an impact its contents could have. World-shattering news, Chamberlain's hopes of peace, along the lines of "I have in my hand a piece of paper…" Think of how life changed, by what was written on it and what was actually executed. Think more intimately, recall exam results, a job, news about health, news about a loved one.

Taking a very deep breath, I opened the thrice-folded thick cream paper. From the long span of a relationship, indeed a lifetime of so many unanswered questions and you have seen there have been many of mine, this was his. In all his loops and convolutions and whorls, in his black ink, Gerald had simply written: *I was the moth. You were the flame.*

In that second, I saw my life, from the moment of first meeting Gerald, had been like a tent, utterly blown away by a strong wind, the guy ropes flailing in the gusts, which one by one I had retrieved. Till that very minute, sitting there in that grey office, occupied by that grey solicitor, I thought I had grasped the last rope from the pulling wind, anchored it back to earth in my hands. But I was wrong.

It was the last line that took my breath away. He had known, indeed assiduously courted it. He had written. *I knew you could do it. What took you so long?*

This book is printed on paper from sustainable sources managed under the Forest Stewardship Council (FSC) scheme.

It has been printed in the UK to reduce transportation miles and their impact upon the environment.

For every new title that Troubador publishes, we plant a tree to offset CO_2, partnering with the More Trees scheme.

For more about how Troubador offsets its environmental impact, see www.troubador.co.uk/sustainability-and-community